OUR MATHEMATICAL HERITAGE

Our Mathematical Heritage

ESSAYS ON THE NATURE AND CULTURAL

SIGNIFICANCE OF MATHEMATICS

Selected and Edited by WILLIAM L. SCHAAF

Professor of Education, Brooklyn College

NEW, REVISED EDITION

COLLIER BOOKS *New York*

COLLIER-MACMILLAN LTD. *London*

Fitz Memorial Library

Endicott Junior College

Beverly, Massachusetts 01915

Copyright © 1963 by William L. Schaaf
All rights reserved. No part of this book may be reproduced or
utilized in any form or by any means, electronic or mechanical,
including photocopying, recording or by any information storage
and retrieval system, without permission in writing from the
Publisher. Library of Congress Catalog Card Number: 62-21525

First Collier Books Edition 1963

Second Printing 1966

This edition, revised for Collier Books, is published by arrangement
with the editor.
The Macmillan Company, New York
Collier-Macmillan Canada Ltd., Toronto, Ontario
Printed in the United States of America

QA
9
S 33
1963

33082

*To Jennie,
a constant source
of encouragement*

6170 RD 1.50

*The nearer man approaches mathematics the far-
ther away he moves from the animals.*

—STANLEY CASSON: *Progress
and Catastrophe*

*. . . even stranger things have happened; and per-
haps the strangest of all is the marvel that mathematics should be possible to a race akin to the
apes.*

—ERIC TEMPLE BELL: *The
Development of Mathematics*

Contents

Preface

MATHEMATICS is an amazing achievement. Like most fundamental things, it defies easy definition, yet it is readily recognized. Mathematics has been variously characterized as unduly recondite, as pure abstraction, and as the apotheosis of
intellectual freedom. But when we have said these things, we
have still not indicated what is mathematics and what is not
mathematics.

Since the dawn of history, with the exception of a few
centuries, there has scarcely been a time when mankind has
not concerned itself with mathematics in one way or
another. This universal interest in mathematics throughout
the ages is rather remarkable. To be sure, as G. H. Hardy
once observed, "most people have some appreciation of
mathematics, just as most people can enjoy a pleasant tune;
and there are probably more people really interested in
mathematics than in music." Yet this general interest, however real, hardly accounts for the high tribute paid to the
mathematician. The man in the street is not particularly
attracted to pure mathematics considered as creative art.
Nor can it be said that mathematics is admired and respected primarily for its service to the arts and sciences. No,
the answer lies elsewhere: the universal homage paid to
mathematics arises from deep human needs that can be satisfied only through mathematical activities.

And just what are mathematical activities? Where do
mathematical concepts come from? Are mathematical ideas
discovered or invented? How is mathematics affected by the
cultural milieu in which it is nurtured? What motivates and
directs the activities of mathematicians? How do they think?
How is mathematics related to physical realities? to creative
art? What are some of the cultural bearings and humanistic
implications of mathematics? What is the basic need that
urges man on in his mathematical activities? What is the
future of mathematics?

It is to seek answers to such questions that these essays
have been brought together. As the late Professor C. J. Keyser once pointed out, the tragedy of modern culture lies in
this: "While the literature of mathematics and mathematical

physics embodies the highest intellectual achievement of man, most of it, unfortunately, is inaccessible to the cultured layman. But even if it were more accessible, I venture to suggest that one might conceivably become familiar with a good deal of it, and still fail to appreciate the intrinsic nature of mathematics and the full import of its cultural significance." To be sure, during the past few decades, a number of valuable contributions have been made by way of filling the gaps deplored by Keyser, notably from the pen of such writers as Edna Kramer, James Newman, W. W. Sawyer, Morris Kline, Jagjit Singh, and Lucienne Félix, among others. Nevertheless, much of the wealth of expository literature of mathematics still remains inconveniently scattered or in inconspicuous places, and it was with these thoughts in mind that the congenial task of assembling the following essays was undertaken.

Obviously, a mere handful of essays, however wisely chosen, cannot do justice to so vast a theme. Moreover, the preferences and frailties of the compiler of an anthology are reflected in his judgment. The choice, in large measure, is necessarily a personal one. Despite these shortcomings, it is to be hoped that the reader will come to appreciate the universal scope of mathematics, the majestic sweep of imagination implied, the boundless heights to which it attains, and the compelling urge felt by its creators. If so, we shall have succeeded in our major purpose: to show that mathematics —man's most daring intellectual achievement—is indeed a wondrous heritage.

W. L. SCHAAF

August 1962

Acknowledgments

THE editor herewith expresses his sincere appreciation of the generous cooperation and the many courtesies extended to him by authors, editors and publishers.

He is especially indebted to George Allen & Unwin, Ltd., Doubleday and Company, Inc., the Harvard University Press, Heinemann Educational Books, Ltd., Alfred A. Knopf, Inc., McGraw-Hill Book Company, the Oxford University Press, the Science Press, and the University of New Mexico Press.

He is also deeply grateful to Dean Elmer C. Easton of the College of Engineering, Rutgers University, and Professor Billy Goetz of the Massachusetts Institute of Technology; to the Mathematical Association of America and to the editors of the *American Mathematical Monthly;* to the National Council of Teachers of Mathematics and to the editors of *The Arithmetic Teacher;* to the Association of Mathematics Teachers of New Jersey and to the editors of the *New Jersey Mathematics Teacher;* and to the editors of *Science and Society* and of the *Scientific Monthly.*

MATHEMATICS AS A
CULTURAL HERITAGE

William L. Schaaf

It has long been my firm conviction that no teacher can do his most effective and creative work without an adequate understanding of the historical development of the subject which he teaches. If so, this may perhaps be even more true for mathematics than for other disciplines. When first published, this essay was addressed primarily to teachers of arithmetic, many of whom are not particularly familiar with the history of that subject. Although the role of arithmetic in particular is here emphasized, the implications for mathematics in general are sufficiently significant to warrant its inclusion in the present volume.

Mathematics as a Cultural Heritage*

BROADLY speaking, major cultures can be identified, at least in part, by certain outstanding characteristics. Thus, Babylonia and Egypt were steeped in mysticism and sensuality; the Greeks were preoccupied with ideas and ideals; the Romans, with politics, military prowess, and conquest. The culture of Western Europe from 600 A.D. to 1100 A.D. was expressed largely by its theology. From 1200 to 1800 it was the exploration of nature and the beginnings of science that marked the essence of the period. The spirit of the nineteenth and twentieth centuries, unless it is too early to judge in proper perspective, is typified by man's increasing mastery over his physical environment. This is evidenced not only by the general achievements of science and technology, but also by unprecedented industrial production, effective mass communication, and increasing automation. The creative language of the culture of today is science, and mathematics is the alphabet of science.

Contributions from the Age of Empiricism in Mathematics

In past ages, mathematics was very largely a tool that not only facilitated the development of a culture, but which was itself more or less shaped by the culture. The pre-Grecian period may be aptly characterized as an age of empiricism in mathematics. Babylonian and Egyptian mathematics were concerned chiefly with astronomical and calendar questions, with the construction of tombs, temples and other religious buildings, and with practical problems of land measurement, surveying, and primitive engineering. In fact, the knowledge of arithmetic and mensuration possessed by the Babylonians appears to have been derived from the earlier work of the Sumerians who preceded them. By 2500 B.C., merchants of Sumer were already thoroughly acquainted with weights and measures, and were using the arithmetic of simple and com-

* Reprinted by permission of the National Council of Teachers of Mathematics and by courtesy of the editors of *The Arithmetic Teacher;* Vol. 8, No. 1, January 1961, pp. 5–9.

pound interest with more than ordinary zeal. The Babylonians were prolific in the creation of elaborate multiplication tables and tables of squares and square roots. They may even have used the zero, although this invention is generally attributed to the Hindus. In short, the Babylonians were very skillful computers.

The Egyptians, whose mathematics was similarly empirical, were likewise adept at calculation. As early as 3500 B.C., they had extended their use of numbers to include hundreds of thousands and millions. Since there was neither inflation nor a national debt, they presumably had little need for billions. The Egyptians revealed an amazing ingenuity in their use of unit fractions; they were aware of the value of checking computation; and there is reason to believe that they anticipated the generalized number concept by using negative numbers as numbers.

Despite the fact that the mathematics of Babylon and Egypt were basically empirical, these two cultures nevertheless left their stamp upon the future in several ways. The idea of number was pressed into service for the market place as well as for the contemplation of the heavens; the idea of geometric form was embraced in practical measurement in surveying, engineering, and astronomy; a distinct if feeble beginning was made in the use of algebraic symbolism; the generalized extension of the system of natural numbers was at least anticipated if not consciously fashioned; and out of experiences with measurement, there grew some awareness of the notion of the mathematical infinite.

The Influence of Greek Contributions and Attitudes

With the ancient Greeks, some six centuries before the Christian era, mathematics came of age. For the next nine hundred years the contributions of Greek culture to mathematics were of the greatest significance, although oddly enough their influence upon arithmetic, as we know it at the present time, was little more than trivial.

It must be appreciated that the Greeks distinguished carefully between two aspects of knowledge about ordinary numbers: *logistiké,* the art of calculating, and *arithmetiké,* an abstract theory of numbers. *Logistica* (in the later Latin form) comprised the techniques of numerical computation in everyday trade and commerce, and in the arts and sciences, including geography and astronomy. *Arithmetica,* on the other hand, dealt with the properties of numbers as such, and in this sense was roughly comparable to contemporary "higher arithmetic" or the elementary theory of numbers (primes, factorization, congruences, etc.). In the eyes of the Greeks, to be concerned with *logistica* was considered beneath the dignity of mathematicians and philosophers, who assigned this drudgery to lesser persons, while they devoted their attention to *arithmetica*, geometry, and philosophy. It should be added that Greek *logistica*, compared to modern methods of computation, was exceedingly cumbersome and crude, due chiefly to an inadequate system of numeration.

These two aspects of the study of numbers were regarded separately until about the time of the invention of printing, although from time to time the names were changed. In the Middle Ages, *logistica*, or "practical arithmetic," was referred to by Italian writers as *practica* or *pratiche;* Latin writers of the Renaissance spoke of the art of computation as *ars supputandi;* Dutch writers called it "ciphering." We still sometimes speak of computing as reckoning, figuring, or calculating; the Germans use the term *Rechnen* for computation, although their term *Arithmetik* covers both aspects. Our modern word "arithmetic" began to be used for both branches in the early part of the sixteenth century.

Not much need be said here about Greek *arithmetiké*. To see it in appropriate perspective, it may be recalled that the Pythagoreans (500 B.C.) divided mathematical studies into four branches, the *quadrivium:* numbers absolute, or *arithmetic;* applied numbers, or *music;* magnitudes at rest, or *geometry;* and magnitudes in motion, or *astronomy.* The weakness of Greek arithmetic lay in the fact that almost from the very beginning, Greek mathematics succumbed to the number mysticism of the oriental cultures. As the centuries slipped by, the superstitious beliefs and esoteric lore associated with numbers increased to the detriment of Greek science and mathematics. Number "magic," *Gematria,* and other precursors of medieval and modern numerology were without doubt one of the facts which prevented the Greeks from embracing algebra and, possibly, even inventing the calculus.

Despite these shortcomings, however, during a period of nearly a thousand years, the Greeks did make several important contributions to arithmetic, or the theory of numbers; for example, (1) they arrived at certain basic theorems concerning the divisibility of numbers; (2) they discovered and proved that the number of primes is infinite; (3) they proved that $\sqrt{2}$ was irrational, and, in general, that the side of a square is incommensurable with its diagonal.

The greatest cultural contribution of the Greeks to mathematics was not their insight into number theory, which, after all, was essentially elementary, nor their skill in the art of computing, which was inconsequential. Their contribution had to do rather with two fundamental concepts or attitudes. One was their faith in the method of deductive reasoning as a sound basis upon which to build the structure of geometry. The other was the belief that our physical environment could be described in mathematical terms; that, in short, number is the language of science. Both legacies were destined to exert a profound influence upon Western civilization for the next two thousand years.

A Barren Period

After the fall of Rome, Western Europe entered upon a period of stagnation and groping for nearly a thousand years. From about 400 to 1500 A.D., mathematics reflected the general cultural condition of the times—meagre and barren. Such as it was, this mathematics was kept alive by a handful of individual laymen and ecclesiastical scholars. One of the earliest influential laymen of this period was Boethius (c.500 A.D.). Among the ecclesiastical mathematicians were Alcuin (c.775), and the French monk Gerbert, who later became pope under the name of Sylvester II (c.1000). Gerbert traveled extensively in Italy and Spain, becoming familiar with Arabic mathematics—especially the Hindu-Arabic numerals.

With the decline of feudalism during the twelfth, thirteenth, and fourteenth centuries there emerged such powerful commercial city-states as Milan, Venice, Florence, Pisa, and Genoa. At the same time, mathematics began to feel the impact of advances in technology and crafts, as well as the effect of a rising trade and money economy. In particular, mathematics was influenced by architecture, military engineering, navigation, and astronomy on the one hand, and, to a lesser extent, by trading, accounts, and commercial activities. The latter involved barter, exchange, customs, drafts, interest, discount, usury, rents, annuities, insurance, partnerships, and stocks. An outstanding writer was Leonardo of Pisa, also known as Fibonacci, whose widely known book,

Liber Abaci (1202), helped spread the Hindu-Arabic system of numeration in Western Europe, but not without considerable resistance.

Introduction of Hindu-Arabic Numerals and a New Interest in Arithmetic

The Hindu-Arabic numerals had found their way into Europe originally through the contacts of traders with Moorish merchants, and through scholars who studied in Spanish universities. At first not well received, their adoption was greatly hindered by inertia and prejudice, and it was not until the sixteenth century that their numerals were in common use throughout Europe.

The fall of the Byzantine Empire, about 1450, saw a revival of interest in mathematics, particularly a study of the original Greek works. Scholarly activities had also moved northward into Central Europe. One of the most influential writers at this time, the German mathematician Regiomontanus, famous for his work in trigonometry, gave considerable impetus to the general interest in mathematics. During the two centuries following Fibonacci, the pace of progress had accelerated: printing had become a fact; the Hindu-Arabic numerals were beginning to take hold; and interest in mathematics was spreading beyond the Italian cities. Close upon the heels of the trigonometry of Regiomontanus came Luca Pacioli's *Summa de Arithmetica* (1494), one of the earliest and most-celebrated printed books on arithmetic. By now the Hindu-Arabic numerals were fairly well established.

Sixteenth-century arithmetic flourished, although new horizons in mathematics also began to dawn. More and more scholars became interested in mathematics; textbooks became more plentiful; interest in science and mechanics increased; and mathematics was being studied for its own sake.

During this fruitful period we find Robert Recorde's *The Ground of Artes* (London, 1540), one of the most popular arithmetics ever printed; the Dutch writer Gemma Frisius, author of a popular text on combined theoretical and commercial arithmetic; Simon Stevin, the Flemish mathematician who was instrumental in furthering the general acceptance of decimal fractions; and John Napier, the aristocratic Scotch baron whose invention of logarithms (1614) was epoch-making. From 1650 to 1850, the interest of mathematicians, having been touched off by the analytic geometry of

Descartes and the calculus of Newton and Leibniz, was focused chiefly upon modern analysis, as well as upon algebra and geometry. As for elementary arithmetic, it was, comparatively speaking, neglected. With the universal acceptance of Hindu-Arabic notation and the recognition of the utility of the decimal notation, the "books were closed" for the time being.

The Dual Role of Arithmetic

Arithmetic from 1850 to the present time may be said to play a dual role in the cultural history of mankind. The more familiar role, and the more prosaic, is that of handmaiden to the arts and sciences, as well as to business. The extraordinary utility of arithmetical computation, as well as of elementary mathematical analysis, has been aptly described by L. Hogben, H. G. Wells, Herbert McKay, and many others. It is a well-known story which need not be reiterated here.

Perhaps the most spectacular development in the field of computation in the last decade or two has been the amazing development of electronic computers. To be sure, both in theory and in practice, these so-called "giant brains" involve far more mathematics than elementary arithmetic. The story of the development of computing machines is a fascinating one, too long to be told here in detail. But it is a far cry from Babbage's "analytic engine" of 1850 to the now famous Eniac of 1950. Ironically enough, our culture, insofar as science and technology are concerned, is now at a point where progress, certainly in some areas, is no longer possible by individual effort alone, but requires the cooperative efforts of a group of related specialists. Thus in developing a typical I.B.M. machine, a fifty-man team may well be used: twenty mathematicians, twenty engineers, and ten technicians. That there is a leader of the team, a person who co-ordinates the work and directs the projects, does not alter the sober fact that no one person can understand all of the theory and intricacies of the machine.

Notably less familiar, at least to the layman, is the second role played by arithmetic in the last hundred years. Yet in many ways it is more subtle and more profound. We refer to the role of arithmetic as catalyst to the comparatively modern examination of the logical foundations of all mathematics, the search for the "structure" of mathematics. This tremendously significant hallmark of twentieth-century mathematics was touched off first by making arithmetic more abstract and generalized, and then by subjecting algebra and analysis to severe "arithmetization." We shall try to make this clear in a few words.

The Search for the Structure of Mathematics

Pythagoras was convinced that all mathematics could be based on the ordinary numbers 1, 2, 3, · · · . Mathematicians of the eighteenth and early nineteenth centuries departed drastically from this naïve point of view by successive extensions of the concept of number from the ordinary whole numbers—extensions to the negative integers and zero, to fractions, to irrationals, to real and to complex numbers—concepts that would doubtless have bewildered Pythagoras. But the middle of the nineteenth century was to witness a revolution: mathematics won a freedom of imagination hitherto unknown. It was anticipated by the invention of non-Euclidean geometry by Lobachevsky and the abstract approach to algebra initiated by Peacock, Gregory, and De Morgan, all in the 1830's. The essence of their approach was to regard geometry and algebra, each respectively as an abstract hypothetico-deductive system in the manner of Euclid. A dozen years later, when Hamilton rejected the commutative law of multiplication (saying in effect, "Let us see what kind of an algebra or arithmetic we get if we assume that $a \times b$ does *not* equal $b \times a$"), the floodgates were opened. From that moment on, mathematicians devoted more and more attention to deliberate generalization and abstraction, exploring the full implications of postulates, and seeking an underlying structure of mathematics.

Contemporary Mathematics

The movement gathered momentum. About 1850, Boole expounded his *Laws of Thought,* foreshadowing modern symbolic logic; about 1875, the nature of the real number system was attacked in earnest by Cantor, Dedekind, Weierstrass, and others. In 1899 the die was cast: Hilbert's logical foundations of geometry sounded the keynote for postulational methods. Accordingly, geometric entities and numbers, as such, became pure abstractions, and the really important question for investigation was the nature and structure of the relations between these abstract concepts. Oddly enough, some ten years earlier, Peano had set forth his set of postulates for common arithmetic and deduced from them, by rigorous logic, the entire body of arithmetic based upon the ordinary, or natural, numbers. So the pendulum returned once more to Pythagoras.

The postulational technique thus initiated proved to be the most powerful single influence of twentieth-century mathematics. Contemporary mathematics is to be distinguished from all previous mathematics in two vital respects: (1) the intentional study of abstractness, where the important considerations are not the things related, but the relations themselves; and (2) the relentless examination of the very foundations—the fundamental ideas—upon which the elaborate superstructure of mathematics is based.

The validity of mathematical reasoning cannot be ascribed to the nature of things; it is due to the very nature of thinking. But the average man or woman does not customarily engage in a level of thinking that involves such abstraction and generalization. It is chiefly for this reason that mathematics repels so many people; the subject is too recondite. In this connection we recall the words of the late Professor C. H. Judd,[1] who reminds us that

> . . . children are not born with a number system as a part of their physical inheritance; they are not endowed at birth with number ideas in any form. The school puts them in contact with a system of number symbols which is one of the most perfect creations of the human mind. In the course of their acquisition of this system, they learn how to think in abstractions with precision. They learn how to use an intellectual device which no single individual, no single generation, could possibly have evolved. In the short span of a few years a child becomes expert in the use of a method of expressing ideas of quantity which cost the race centuries of time and effort to invent and perfect.

Mathematics is a linguistic activity; its ultimate aim is preciseness of communication. Second only to the mother tongue, the language of number is without doubt the greatest

[1] Charles H. Judd, *Educational Psychology* (New York: Houghton Mifflin, 1939), p. 270.

symbolic creation of man. And in some ways it is an even more effective agency of communication than the vernacular. In short, mathematics is a great cultural heritage, and although the beginnings have been lost in the mists of time, it is a heritage we should be proud to transmit to the world of tomorrow.

ON THE DEVELOPMENT OF
MATHEMATICS

ERIC TEMPLE BELL

The past hundred years have witnessed the coming of the Golden Age of mathematics. Nothing that happened during the previous six thousand years can remotely approach in daring and in vastness this stupendous development. Contemporary mathematics is at once a triumphant achievement and an unbelievable heritage.

From whence did this magnificent creation spring? The question is not easily answered. While some scholars regard the development of mathematical knowledge as an essentially continuous evolution, others (for example, Spengler) hold that what we call "mathematics" consists of several discrete, individual developments, each manifesting its own birth, growth, and eventual decay.

The late Professor Bell needs no introduction to American readers. His Queen of the Sciences *is a priceless gem; his* Men of Mathematics *has become a classic. Other well-known works include* Numerology, Handmaiden of the Sciences, The Search for Truth, The Magic of Numbers, *and* The Last Problem. *His incisive exposition and inimitable style unquestionably mark him as one of the foremost American writers on expository mathematics.*

On the Development of Mathematics*

IN ALL historic times all civilized peoples have striven toward mathematics. The prehistoric origins are as irrecoverable as those of language and art, and even the civilized beginnings can only be conjectured from the behavior of primitive peoples today. Whatever its source, mathematics has come down to the present by the two main streams of number and form. The first carried along arithmetic and algebra, the second, geometry. In the seventeenth century these two united, forming the ever-broadening river of mathematical analysis.

Five Streams

Into the two main streams of number and form flowed many tributaries. At first mere trickles, some quickly swelled to the dignity of independent rivers. Two in particular influenced the whole course of mathematics from almost the earliest recorded history to the twentieth century. Counting by the natural numbers 1, 2, 3, . . . introduced mathematicians to the concept of *discreteness*. The invention of irrational numbers, such as $\sqrt{2}$, $\sqrt{3}$, $\sqrt{6}$; attempts to compute plane areas bounded by curves or by incommensurable straight lines; the like for surfaces and volumes; also a long struggle to give a coherent account of motion, growth, and other sensually continuous change, forced mathematicians to invent the concept of *continuity*.

The whole of mathematical history may be interpreted as a battle for supremacy between these two concepts. This conflict may be but an echo of the older strife so prominent in early Greek philosophy, the struggle of the One to subdue the Many. But the image of a battle is not wholly appropriate, in mathematics at least, as the continuous and the discrete have frequently helped one another to progress.

One type of mathematical mind prefers the problems associated with continuity. Geometers, analysts, and appliers of mathematics to science and technology are of this type. The

---

* By permission, from E. T. Bell, *The Development of Mathematics.* Copyright, 1940, by McGraw-Hill Book Co., Inc.

complementary type, preferring discreteness, takes naturally to the theory of numbers in all its ramifications, to algebra, and to mathematical logic. No sharp line divides the two, and the master mathematicians have worked with equal ease in both the continuous and the discrete.

In addition to number, form, discreteness, and continuity, a fifth stream has been of capital importance in mathematical history, especially since the seventeenth century. As the sciences, beginning with astronomy and engineering in ancient times and ending with biology, psychology, and sociology in our own, became more and more exact, they made constantly increasing demands on mathematical inventiveness, and were mainly responsible for a large part of the enormous expansion of all mathematics since 1637. Again, as industry and invention became increasingly scientific after the industrial revolution of the late eighteenth and early nineteenth centuries, they too stimulated mathematical creation, often posing problems beyond the existing resources of mathematics. A current instance is the problem of turbulent flow, of the first importance in aerodynamics. Here, as in many similar situations, attempts to solve an essentially new technological problem have led to further expansions of pure mathematics.

The Time-scale

It will be well to have some idea of the distribution of mathematics in time before looking at individual advances.

The time curve of mathematical productivity is roughly similar to the exponential curve of biologic growth, starting to rise almost imperceptibly in the remote past and shooting up with ever greater rapidity as the present is approached. The curve is by no means smooth; for, like art, mathematics has had its depressions. There was a deep one in the Middle Ages, owing to the mathematical barbarism of Europe being only partly balanced by the Moslem civilization, itself (mathematically) a sharp recession from the great epoch (third century B.C.) of Archimedes. But in spite of depressions, the general trend from the past to the present has been in the upward direction of a steady increase of valid mathematics.

We should not expect the curve for mathematics to follow those of other civilized activities, say art and music, too closely. Masterpieces of sculpture once shattered are difficult to restore or even to remember. The greater ideas of mathematics survive and are carried along in the continual flow, permanent additions immune to the accidents of fashion. Being expressed in the one universally intelligible language as yet devised by human beings, the creations of mathematics are independent of national taste, as those of literature are not. Who today except a few scholars is interested or amused by the ancient Egyptian novelette of the two thieves? And how many can understand hieroglyphics sufficiently to elicit from the story whatever significance it may once have had for a people dead all of three thousand years? But tell any engineer, or any schoolboy who has had some mensuration, the Egyptian rule for the volume of a truncated square pyramid, and he will recognize it instantly. Not only are the valid creations of mathematics preserved; their mere presence in the stream of progress induces new currents of mathematical thought.

The majority of working mathematicians acquainted in some measure with the mathematics created since 1800 agree that the time curve rises more sharply thereafter than before. An open mind on this question is necessary for anyone wishing to see mathematical history as the majority of mathematicians see it. Many who have no firsthand knowledge of living mathematics beyond the calculus believe on grossly inadequate evidence that mathematics experienced its golden age in some more or less remote past. Mathematicians think not. The recent era, beginning in the nineteenth century, is usually regarded as the golden age by those personally conversant with mathematics and at least some of its history.

An unorthodox but reasonable apportionment of the time-scale of mathematical development cuts all history into three periods of unequal lengths. These may be called the remote, the middle, and the recent. The remote extends from the earliest times of which we have reliable knowledge to A.D. 1637, the middle from 1638 to 1800. The recent period, that of modern mathematics as professionals today understand mathematics, extends from 1801 to the present. Some might prefer 1821 instead of 1801.

There are definite reasons for the precise dates. Geometry became analytic in 1637 with the publication of Descartes' masterpiece. About half a century later the calculus of Newton and Leibniz, also the dynamics of Galileo and Newton, began to become the common property of all creative mathematicians. Leibniz certainly was competent to estimate the magnitude of this advance. He is reported to have said that, of all mathematics from the beginning of the world to the time of Newton, what Newton had done was much the better half.

The eighteenth century exploited the methods of Descartes, Newton, and Leibniz in all departments of mathematics as they then existed. Perhaps the most significant feature of this century was the beginning of the abstract, completely general attack. Although adequate realization of the power of the abstract method was delayed till the twentieth century, there are notable anticipations in Lagrange's work on algebraic equations and, above all, in his analytic mechanics. In the latter, a direct, universal method unified mechanics as it then was, and has remained to this day one of the most powerful tools in the physical sciences. There was nothing like this before Lagrange.

The last date, 1801, marks the beginning of a new era of unprecedented inventiveness, opening with the publication of Gauss' masterpiece. The alternative, 1821, is the year in which Cauchy began the first satisfactory treatment of the differential and integral calculus.

As one instance of the greatly accelerated productivity in the nineteenth century, consequent to a thorough mastery and amplification of the methods devised in the middle period, an episode in the development of geometry is typical. Each of five men—Lobachevsky, Bolyai, Plücker, Riemann, Lie—invented as part of his lifework as much (or more) new geometry as was created by all the Greek mathematicians in the two or three centuries of their greatest activity. There are good grounds for the frequent assertion that the nineteenth century alone contributed about five times as much to mathematics as had all preceding history. This applies not only to quantity but, what is of incomparably greater importance, to power.

Granting that the mathematicians before the middle period may have encountered the difficulties attendant on all pioneering, we need not magnify their great achievements to universe-filling proportions. It must be remembered that the advances of the recent period have swept up and included nearly all the valid mathematics that preceded 1800 as very special instances of general theories and methods. Of course nobody who works in mathematics believes that our age has reached the end, as Lagrange thought his had just before the great outburst of the recent period. But this does not alter the fact that most of our predecessors did reach very definite ends, as we too no doubt shall. Their limited methods precluded further significant progress, and it is possible, let us hope probable, that a century hence our own more powerful methods will have given place to others yet more powerful.

Seven Periods

A more conventional division of the time-scale separates all mathematical history into seven periods:

(1) From the earliest times to ancient Babylonia and Egypt, inclusive.

(2) The Greek contribution, about 600 B.C. to about A.D. 300, the best being in the fourth and third centuries B.C.

(3) The oriental and Semitic peoples—Hindus, Chinese, Persians, Moslems, Jews, etc., partly before, partly after (2), and extending to (4).

(4) Europe during the Renaissance and the Reformation, roughly the fifteenth and sixteenth centuries.

(5) The seventeenth and eighteenth centuries.

(6) The nineteenth century.

(7) The twentieth century.

This division follows loosely the general development of Western civilization and its indebtedness to the Near East. Possibly (6), (7) are only one, although profoundly significant new trends became evident shortly after 1900. . . .

Although the peoples of the Near East were more active than the Europeans during the third of the seven periods, mathematics as it exists today is predominantly a product of Western civilization. Ancient advances in China, for example, either did not enter the general stream or did so by commerce not yet traced. Even such definite techniques as were devised either belong to the trivia of mathematics or were withheld from European mathematicians until long after their demonstrably independent invention in Europe. For example, Horner's method for the numerical solution of equations may have been known to the Chinese, but Horner did not know that it was. And, as a matter of fact, mathematics would not be much the poorer if neither the Chinese nor Horner had ever hit on the method.

European mathematics followed a course approximately parallel to that of the general culture in the several countries.

Thus the narrowly practical civilization of ancient Rome contributed nothing to mathematics; when Italy was great in art, it excelled in algebra; when the last surge of the Elizabethan age in England had spent itself, supremacy in mathematics passed to Switzerland and France. Frequently, however, there were sporadic outbursts of isolated genius in politically minor countries, as in the independent creation of non-Euclidean geometry in Hungary in the early nineteenth century. Sudden upsurges of national vitality were occasionally accompanied by increased mathematical activity, as in the Napoleonic wars following the French Revolution, also in Germany after the disturbances of 1848. But the world war of 1914–18 appears to have been a brake on mathematical progress in Europe and to a lesser degree elsewhere, as also were the subsequent manifestations of nationalism in Russia, Germany, and Italy. These events hastened the rapid progress which mathematics had been making since about 1890 in the United States of America, thrusting that country into a leading position.

The correlation between mathematical excellence and brilliance in other aspects of general culture was sometimes negative. Several instances might be given; the most important for the development of mathematics falls in the Middle Ages. When Gothic architecture and Christian civilization were at their zenith in the twelfth century (some would say in the thirteenth), European mathematics was just beginning the ascent from its nadir. It will be extremely interesting to historians eight centuries hence if it shall appear that the official disrepute into which mathematics and impartial science had fallen in certain European countries some years before the triumph of medieval ideals in September, 1939, was the dawn of a new faith about to enshrine itself in the unmathematical simplicities of a scienceless architecture. Our shaggy ancestors got along for hundreds of thousands of years without science or mathematics in their filthy caves, and there is no obvious reason why our brutalized descendants—if they are to be such—should not do the same.

Attending here only to acquisitions of the very first magnitude in all seven of the periods, we may signalize three. . . .

The most enduringly influential contribution to mathematics of all the periods prior to the Renaissance was the Greek invention of strict deductive reasoning. Next in mathematical importance is the Italian and French development of symbolic algebra during the Renaissance. The Hindus of the seventh to the twelfth century A.D. had almost invented algebraic symbolism; the Moslems reverted in their classic age to an almost completely rhetorical algebra. The third major advance has already been indicated, but may be emphasized here: in the earlier part of the fifth period—seventeenth century—the three main streams of number, form, and continuity united. This generated the calculus and mathematical analysis in general; it also transformed geometry and made possible the later creation of the higher spaces necessary for modern applied mathematics. The leaders here were French, English, and German.

The fifth period is usually considered as the fountainhead of modern pure mathematics. It brackets the beginning of modern science; and another major advance was the extensive application of the newly created pure mathematics to dynamical astronomy, following the work of Newton, and, a little later, to the physical sciences, following the methodology of Galileo and Newton. Finally, in the nineteenth century, the great river burst its banks, deluging wildernesses where no mathematics had flourished and making them fruitful.

If the mathematics of the twentieth century differs significantly from that of nineteenth, possibly the most important distinctions are a marked increase in abstractness with a consequent gain in generality, and a growing preoccupation with the morphology and comparative anatomy of mathematical structures; a sharpening of critical insight; and a dawning recognition of the limitations of classical deductive reasoning. If "limitations" suggests frustration after about seven thousand years of human strivings to think clearly, the suggestion is misleading. But it is true that the critical evaluations of accepted mathematical reasoning which distinguished the first four decades of the twentieth century necessitated extensive revisions of earlier mathematics, and inspired much new work of profound interest for both mathematics and epistemology. They also led to what appeared to be the final abandonment of the theory that mathematics is an image of the Eternal Truth.

The division of mathematical history into about seven periods is more or less traditional and undoubtedly is illuminating, especially in relation to the fluctuating light which we call civilization. But the unorthodox remote, middle, and recent periods, described earlier, seem to give a truer presentation of the development of mathematics itself and a more vivid suggestion of its innate vitality.

Some General Characteristics

In each of the seven periods there was a well-defined rise to maturity and a subsequent decline in each of several limited modes of mathematical thought. Without fertilization by creative new ideas, each was doomed to sterility. In the Greek period, for example, synthetic metric geometry, as a method, got as far as seems humanly possible with our present mental equipment. It was revivified into something new by the ideas of analytic geometry in the seventeenth century, by those of projective geometry in the seventeenth and nineteenth centuries, and finally, in the eighteenth and nineteenth centuries, by those of differential geometry.

Such revitalizations were necessary not only for the continued growth of mathematics but also for the development of science. Thus it would be impossible for mathematicians to apprehend the subtle complexities of the geometries applied to modern science by the methods of Euclid and Apollonius. And in pure mathematics, much of the geometry of the nineteenth century was thrust aside by the more vigorous geometries of abstract spaces and the non-Riemannian geometries developed in the twentieth. Considerably less than forty years after the close of the nineteenth century, some of the geometrical masterpieces of that heroic age of geometry were already beginning to seem otiose and antiquated. This appears to be the case for much of classical differential geometry and synthetic projective geometry. If mathematics continues to advance, the new geometries of the twentieth century will likely be displaced in their turn, or be subsumed under still rarer abstractions. In mathematics, of all places, finality is a chimera. Its rare appearances are witnessed only by the mathematically dead.

As a period closes, there is a tendency to overelaboration of merely difficult things which the succeeding period either ignores as unlikely to be of lasting value, or includes as exercises in more powerful methods. Thus a host of special curves investigated with astonishing vigor and enthusiasm by the early masters of analytic geometry live, if at all, only as problems in elementary textbooks. Perhaps the most extensive of all mathematical cemeteries are the treatises which perpetuate artifically difficult problems in mechanics to be worked as if Lagrange, Hamilton, and Jacobi had never lived.

Again, as we approach the present, new provinces of mathematics are more and more rapidly stripped of their superficial riches, leaving only a hypothetical mother lode to be sought by the better-equipped prospectors of a later generation. The law of diminishing returns operates here in mathematics as in economics: without the introduction of radically new improvements in method, the income does not balance the outgo. A conspicuous example is the highly developed theory of algebraic invariants, one of the major acquisitions of the nineteenth century; another, the classical theory of multiply periodic functions, of the same century. The first of these contributed indirectly to the emergence of general relativity; the second inspired much work in analysis and algebraic geometry.

A last phenomenon of the entire development may be noted. At first the mathematical disciplines were not sharply defined. As knowledge increased, individual subjects split off from the parent mass and became autonomous. Later, some were overtaken and reabsorbed in vaster generalizations of the mass from which they had sprung. Thus trigonometry issued from surveying, astronomy, and geometry only to be absorbed, centuries later, in the analysis which had generalized geometry.

This recurrent escape and recapture has inspired some to dream of a final, unified mathematics which shall embrace all. Early in the twentieth century it was believed by some for a time that the desired unification had been achieved in mathematical logic. But mathematics, too irrepressibly creative to be restrained by any formalism, escaped.

Motivation in Mathematics

Several items in the foregoing prospectus suggest that much of the impulse behind mathematics has been economic. In the third and fourth decades of the twentieth century, for obvious political reasons, attempts were made to show that all vital mathematics, particularly in applications, is of economic origin.

To overemphasize the immediately practical in the development of mathematics at the expense of sheer intellectual curiosity is to miss at least half the fact. As any moderately competent mathematician whose education has not stopped short with the calculus and its commoner applications may verify for himself, it simply is not true that the economic motive has been more frequent than the purely intellectual in the creation of mathematics. This holds for practical mathematics as applied in commerce, including all insurance, science, and the technologies, as well as for those divisions of mathematics which at present are economically valueless. Instances might be multiplied indefinitely; four must suffice here, one from the theory of numbers, two from geometry, and one from algebra.

About twenty centuries before the polygonal numbers were generalized, and considerably later applied to insurance and to statistics, in both instances through combinatorial analysis, the former by way of the mathematical theory of probability, their amusing peculiarities were extensively investigated by arithmeticians without the least suspicion that far in the future these numbers were to prove useful in practical affairs. The polygonal numbers appealed to the Pythagoreans of the sixth century B.C. and to their bemused successors on account of the supposedly mystical virtues of such numbers. The impulse here might be called religious. Anyone familiar with the readily available history of these numbers and acquainted with Plato's dialogues can trace for himself the thread of number mysticism from the crude numerology of the Pythagoreans to the Platonic doctrine of Ideas. None of this greatly resembles insurance or statistics.

Later mathematicians, including one of the greatest, regarded these numbers as legitimate objects of intellectual curiosity. Fermat, cofounder with Pascal in the seventeenth century of the mathematical theory of probability, and therefore one of the grandfathers of insurance, amused himself with the polygonal and figurate numbers for years before either he or Pascal ever dreamed of defining probability mathematically.

As a second and somewhat hackneyed instance, the conic sections were substantially exhausted by the Greeks about seventeen centuries before their application to ballistics and astronomy, and through the latter to navigation, were suspected. These applications might have been made without the Greek geometry, had Descartes' analytics and Newton's dynamics been available. But the fact is that by heavy borrowings from Greek conics the right way was first found. Again the initial motive was intellectual curiosity.

The third instance is that of polydimensional space. In analytic geometry, a plane curve is represented by an equation containing two variables, a surface by an equation containing three. Cayley in 1843 transferred the language of geometry to systems of equations in more than three variables, thus inventing a geometry of any finite number of dimensions. This generalization was suggested directly by the formal algebra of common analytic geometry, and was elaborated for its intrinsic interest before uses for it were found in thermodynamics, statistical mechanics, and other departments of science, including statistics, both theoretical and industrial as in applied physical chemistry. In passing, it may be noted that one method in statistical mechanics makes incidental use of the arithmetical theory of partitions, which treats of such problems as determining in how many ways a given positive integer is a sum of positive integers. This theory was initiated by Euler in the eighteenth century, and for over 150 years was nothing but a plaything for experts in the perfectly useless theory of numbers.

The fourth instance concerns abstract algebra as it has developed since 1910. Any modern algebraist may easily verify that much of his work has a main root in one of the most fantastically useless problems ever imagined by curious man, namely, in Fermat's famous assertion of the seventeenth century that $x^n + y^n = z^n$ is impossible in integers x, y, z, all different from zero if n is an integer greater than two. Some of this recent algebra quickly found use in the physical sciences, particularly in modern quantum mechanics. It was developed without any suspicion that it might be scientifically useful. Indeed, not one of the algebraists concerned was competent to make any significant application of his work to science, much less to foresee that such applications would some day be possible. As late as the autumn of 1925, only two or three physicists in the entire world had any inkling of the new channel much of physics was to follow in 1926 and the succeeding decade.

Residues of Epochs

In following the development of mathematics, or of any science, it is essential to remember that although some particular work may now be buried it is not necessarily dead. Each epoch has left a mass of detailed results, most of which are now of only antiquarian interest. For the remoter periods, these survive as curiosities in specialized histories of mathematics. For the middle and recent periods—since the early decades of the seventeenth century—innumerable theorems and even highly developed theories are entombed in the technical journals and transactions of learned societies, and are seldom if ever mentioned even by professionals. The mere existence of many is all but forgotten. The lives of thousands of workers have gone into this moribund literature. In what sense do these half-forgotten things live? And how can it be truthfully said that the labor of all those toilers was not wasted?

The answers to these somewhat discouraging questions are obvious to anyone who works in mathematics. Out of all the uncoordinated details at last emerges a general method or a new concept. The method or the concept is what survives. By means of the general method the laborious details from which it evolved are obtained uniformly and with comparative ease. The new concept is seen to be more significant for the whole of mathematics than are the obscure phenomena from which it was abstracted. But such is the nature of the human mind that it almost invariably takes the longest way round, shunning the straight road to its goal. There is no principle of least action in scientific discovery. Indeed, the goal in mathematics frequently is unperceived until some explorer more fortunate than his rivals blunders onto it in spite of his human inclination to follow the crookedest path. Simplicity and directness are usually the last things to be attained.

In illustration of these facts we may cite once more the theory of algebraic invariants. When this theory was first developed in the nineteenth century, scores of devoted workers slaved at the detailed calculation of particular invariants and covariants. Their work is buried. But its very complexity drove their successors in algebra to simplicity: masses of apparently isolated phenomena were recognized as instances of simple underlying general principles. Whether these principles would ever have been sought, much less discovered, without the urge imparted by the massed calculations, is at least debatable. The historical fact is that they were so sought and discovered.

In saying that the formidable lists of covariants and invariants of the early period are buried, we do not mean to imply that they are permanently useless; for the future of mathematics is as unpredictable as is that of any other social activity. But the methods and principles of the later period make it possible to obtain all such results with much greater ease should they ever be required, and it is a waste of time and effort today to add to them.

One residue of all this vast effort is the concept of invariance. So far as can be seen at present, invariance is likely to be illuminating in both pure and applied mathematics for many decades to come. . . . It is not epochs that matter, but their residues. Nor, as epochs recede into the past, do the men who made them obscure the permanence and impersonality of their work with their hopes, their fears, their jealousies, and their petty quarrels. Some of the greatest things that were ever done in mathematics are wholly anonymous. We shall never know who first imagined the numbers 1, 2, 3, . . . , or who first perceived that a single "three" isolates what is common to three goads, three oxen, three gods, three altars, and three men.

ON THE GENESIS OF
MATHEMATICAL IDEAS

GEORGE SARTON

Probably no subject loses so much as mathematics when it is dissociated from its history. We might also assert, as George Sarton has done elsewhere, that "the history of mathematics should really be the kernel of the history of culture." For the roots of mathematical progress reach back to the groping from which primitive man at last emerged; and the subsequent development of mathematics permeates all cultures of which we have any record.

Professor Sarton suggests that the spirit of self-criticism that has pervaded mathematics for the past fifty years may prove to have been the preparation for undreamed-of new adventures; on the other hand, the sequel may bring little of significance. It is too early to tell. At all events, the well-springs of mathematical creation are here brilliantly analyzed by a master historian. His thesis is that, while mathematical creations and discoveries are shaped to some extent by external forces, the main source of mathematical achievement lies within man himself—is, indeed, a reflection of the spirit of freedom peculiar to the mind and soul of man.

A gifted and profound scholar, the late Dr. Sarton was one of the world's foremost authorities on the history of science and mathematics.

On the Genesis of
Mathematical Ideas*

THE HISTORY of mathematics is exhilarating, because it unfolds before us the vision of an endless series of victories of the human mind, victories without counterbalancing failures, that is, without dishonorable and humiliating ones, and without atrocities. At the same time it helps to dispel pessimism. However great the victories may be, the seasoned historian expects still more and greater ones. Has it not always been so? Has not each mathematical conquest been followed with another and nobler one? History shows that time after time a theory which was thought final and complete was nothing but a stepping stone to a better one, and new theories were thus established one after another when there seemed to be no more room for them. Why should the future be essentially different from the past? Why should our presence to-day create such a strange discontinuity in human evolution? It is thus highly probable that mathematics will continue to be unfolded with greater and greater exuberance. There may be now and then periods of rest and fallow, but it is almost inconceivable that our knowledge should ever be everywhere lost and permanently stopped. It cannot decrease, it is bound to increase, though no one can foretell the rate of growth.

The process of growing abstraction, diversity, and complexity which began in prehistoric days when the idea of number was adumbrated, and which has never since been completely checked, will continue. There is no reason why it should not. The mathematical field has been enormously enlarged, it is true, but the larger the field, the greater, not smaller, are the opportunities; the longer the frontiers of science, the more space there is for new departures into the unknown. On the basis of my historical experience, I fully believe that mathematics of the twenty-fifth century will be as different from that of to-day as the latter is from that of the sixteenth century.

* From George Sarton, *The Study of the History of Mathematics,* 1936, pp. 13–25. By permission of the Harvard University Press.

In the meanwhile, our intellectual wealth is becoming truly embarrassing. The mathematical universe is already so large and diversified that it is hardly possible for a single mind to grasp it, or, to put it in another way, so much energy would be needed for grasping it that there would be none left for creative research. A mathematical congress of to-day reminds one of the Tower of Babel, for few men can follow profitably the discussions of sections other than their own, and even there they are sometimes made to feel like strangers. In consequence, the explorer and the conqueror are condemned to relative ignorance and blindness, and they become less and less able to complete their task without guidance from others. This illustrates in another way the increasing need of mathematical surveys, historical analyses, philosophical elaborations.

No thinking man can contemplate the mathematical past without asking himself some fundamental questions, which are as simple to formulate as they are difficult to answer. To what extent were the filiation and development of ideas determined either by outside circumstances or by a kind of internal necessity? An extreme answer to that question was suggested by Évariste Galois:

> La science progresse par une série de combinaisons où le hazard ne joue pas le moindre rôle; sa vie est brute et ressemble à celle des minéraux qui croissent par juxtà position. Celà s'applique non seulement à la science telle qu'elle résulte des travaux d'une série de savants, mais aussi aux recherches particulières à chacun d'eux. En vain les analystes voudraient-ils se le dissimuler: ils ne déduisent pas, ils combinent, ils comparent; quand ils arrivent à la vérité, c'est en heurtant de côté et d'autre qu'il y sont tombés.[1]

There is no doubt that Galois's curious answer was itself dominated by an internal necessity, by the merciless genius in him which left him no choice but to obey. He must have felt strongly the hopelessness of resisting one's fate. As to external necessities, very clear answers on the subject have been given us repeatedly by mathematicians of the new Russian persuasion. According to them, even Newton's achievement was conditioned by the economic needs of his time. And yet

I am not convinced. It is easy enough to explain some facts retrospectively, especially if one be free to select the convenient facts and to abandon the inconvenient ones. Why did the most industrial and mercantile nation of Europe reject the metric system, while its use would have caused great economies in time and money? Suppose the situation had been reversed, how tempting it would have been to explain the creation of the metric system as a necessary result of the superior mercantilism of England.

There is no doubt that mathematical discoveries are conditioned by outside events of every kind, political, economic, scientific, military, and by the incessant demands of the arts of peace and war. Mathematics did never develop in a political or economic vacuum. However, we think that those events were only some of the factors among others, factors the power of which might vary and did vary from time to time. It might be almost decisive in one case, and ineffectual in another.

Even the internal necessity, though much stronger than the external one, might be inoperative. While the properties of ellipses were revealed in the second half of the third century B.C. by the genius of Apollonius, astronomers continued for more than eighteen centuries to account for the erratic motions of the planets by complicated systems of epicycles and eccentrics. Granted that the problem of finding the earth's trajectory was exceedingly difficult,[2] Kepler's achievement might have occurred much earlier. One would have thought that the concept of the ellipse would have been strong enough to impose itself on men's minds and to find for itself beautiful applications.

The historian is unable to dictate how things will happen or should happen; he must be satisfied to describe humbly enough how they did happen. He naturally tries to arrange events in causal sequences, but he should never indulge in dogmatism on the subject.

The main sources of mathematical invention seem to be within man rather than outside of him: his own inveterate and insatiable curiosity, his constant itching for intellectual adventure; and likewise the main obstacles to mathematical progress seem to be also within himself; his scandalous inertia and laziness, his fear of adventure, his need of conformity to old standards, and his obsession by mathematical ghosts. It is true these ghosts may sometimes suggest valuable applications and survive. For example, the shadow of the unitary fractions of the Egyptians influenced mathematics for centuries and impeded its progress, but they suggested incidentally the *fractiones in gradibus* of Leonardo Fibonacci (1202) and the continued fractions of later times.[3] Our mathematical practice of to-day is still littered with the fossils of earlier times, such as Roman numerals, sexagesimal fractions, the English weights and measures, etc.; on the other hand, other relics have been abandoned, the rediscovery of which delights the historian, even as obsolete curios delight the archaeologist. When we compare the whole of mankind with a single man growing in knowledge and wisdom, we may stretch the comparison a little further: no man remembers equally well everything; even the best memory experiences lapses, betrayals, and preferences. The whole of mankind is like a man with a memory that is good but not perfect.

The deterministic theory of mathematical progress remains insufficient even when one has corrected and tempered it as we have done. It is not always possible to account for the development of mathematical ideas by a combination of external events with personal impulses on the one hand and personal inhibitions on the other, great as is the flexibility of such a method. There are many facts which one cannot account for in a general way, and this applies to mathematical inventions as well as to any other details of human behavior. Many mathematical developments are capricious in the extreme, and it is a waste of time to try to find a rational explanation of them. Strangely enough, in the same text wherein Galois expressed so strongly his belief in mathematical fatality, he also called attention to the great irregularity and disorder of our mathematical knowledge. An orderly development would only be possible for a godlike mathematician knowing in advance all the possible mathematics.

Here is really the crux of the matter. Mathematicians and other scientists, however great they may be, do not know the future. Their genius may enable them to project their purpose ahead of them; it is as if they had a special lamp, unavailable to lesser men, illuminating their path; but even in the most favorable cases the lamp sends only a very small cone of light into the infinite darkness. Enthusiastic admirers of great men often make the mistake of giving them credit for the endless consequences of their discoveries, consequences which they could not possibly foresee. To credit Galois with all the results of the theory of groups is as foolish as to credit Faraday with all the wonders of electrotechnics, or to hold Columbus responsible for all the good and evil done in the New World since 1492. The founder of a new theory or of a new science deserves full credit for the discoveries which he actually made, less credit for those which he adumbrated, and still less for those which he made possible but did not realize. While we honor him as a founder, we must remember that he could not possibly anticipate all the consequences of his ideas and all the fruits of his deeds. He is the spiritual lord of the domain which his imagination could encompass, neither more nor less. We often call him the father of this or that, and such a term is appropriate enough to express our respect, even our veneration, if we bear in mind that parents should not be praised or blamed too much for their children, though they made them, not to speak of their more distant descendants who sprang from other loins.

The capriciousness of mathematical development cannot be emphasized too much. Why were the early Greeks so interested in the theory of numbers, and so little in plain arithmetic? The latter was highly needed. Every reason of economic necessity should have caused the development of arithmetic, and discouraged as a luxury the growth of fanciful ideas on the properties of numbers. Why did magic squares interest so many peoples East and West? Why? Why? The student of history should not ask such childish queries. His purpose cannot be to give a completely logical account of the past, for such account is obviously out of the question. It is only here and there that a few logical knots can be tied; for the rest, we must be satisfied with a faithful description of the possibilities which materialized among an infinity of others which did not. The shortest distance from one point to another is a geodetic line, but such a line can only be followed if one knows one's destination, in which case there would be no discovery. The ways of discovery must necessarily be very different from the shortest way, indirect and circuitous, with many windings and retreats. It is only at a later stage of knowledge, when a new domain has been sufficiently explored, that it becomes possible to reconstruct the whole theory on a logical basis, and to show how it might have been discovered by an omniscient being, that is, how it might have been discovered if there had been no real need of discovering it! Galois's impatience with the textbooks of his day was inconsistent. It is as if an explorer of an unknown territory complained of the absence of maps, or the student of an unknown language of the lack of grammars and dictionaries.

To conclude, capriciousness is of the essence of discovery, because we can only know where we are going, and whether it is worth going to, when we are there. Accordingly we cannot help following many false trails, and going astray in many ways. Moreover, caprice is of the essence of life in general, and of human life in particular, because of life's very complexity and indetermination.

Nevertheless, the development of mathematics is perhaps less capricious than that of other sciences, more completely determined (or less undetermined), if not by external factors, at least by internal ones, for each theory presses forward as it were, and the mathematicians who are playing with it must needs perceive some of its consequences. The desire to follow them to the limit is then likely to prove irresistible, whether these consequences be useful or not. The concatenations of mathematical ideas are not divorced from life, far from it, but they are less influenced than other scientific ideas by accidents, and it is perhaps more possible, and more permissible, for a mathematician than for any other man to secrete himself in a tower of ivory.

The history of mathematics is thus a good field for the investigation of theories concerning the progress of science in general, and the possibilities of logical development in particular. It is conceivable that the capriciousness is only relative after all, that it affects the details of the picture rather than the main outline. Such a conception is attractive enough to be fully investigated, and only the historian can do it. The vicissitudes of history might be overlooked in a first approximation. One might assume that Man (not this man or that, whatever be his genius) followed unerringly the geodetic line from A to B (A and B being two mathematical discoveries) instead of meandering and beating about the bush.

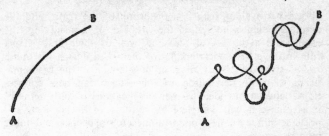

This assumption, in fact, the historian of mathematics is often obliged to make, if only for the sake of brevity and simplicity. Reality is far too complex to be represented to the last detail, but the historian's simplification must remain sufficiently close to it; it must represent the main outline in chronological sequence. It is thus exceedingly different from the synthetic reconstruction made by teachers, wherein the chronological sequence is necessarily disregarded as irrelevant. The mathematician whose privilege it is to give to a theory its final, "classical" shape, is likely to define the function he is dealing with by means of the property which was perhaps the last one to be discovered. That is all right: the synthesis thus created, however distant it may be from historical contingencies, is closer to the deeper mathematical realities.

We need equally the two kinds of synthesis: the historical and the purely mathematical. The latter is the shortest if not always the easiest path to knowledge, but it fails to explain the human implications; it may satisfy the matter-of-fact and hurried mathematician; it cannot satisfy the philosopher and the humanist.

As to the pure mathematician, even he should not be too easily satisfied with the latest synthesis. To begin with, that synthesis may be incomplete. Some elements which were not deemed essential for it may have other values, they may prove to be essential for other structures, or the one from which they were eliminated may not be as final as it seems. Indeed, no theory is ever final. A new discovery, a new point of view may cause its abandonment and its supersedure by another, and the facts neglected in one shuffling may be considered invaluable in another. Every synthesis implies sacrifices; it is not merely a simplification but also and unavoidably a betrayal of reality, a distortion of the truth, and the mathematician who takes the trouble of considering the origin and evolution of ideas, as well as their final shape, will improve his understanding of them and enrich his mind.

The study of history may, or may not, help the mathematician to make new discoveries by suggesting new connections between old ideas or new applications of old methods; in any case it will complete his mastery of the subject, and provide him with new opportunities for a deeper and more intuitive grasp of it.

The main reason for studying the history of mathematics, or the history of any science, is purely humanistic. Being men, we are interested in other men, and especially in such men as have helped us to fulfil our highest destiny. As soon as we realize the great part played by individual men in mathematical discoveries—for, however these may be determined, they cannot be brought about except by means of human brains—we are anxious to know all their circumstances.[4] How did it happen that this man or that man, among others, was devoted to mathematics? Was he thus consecrated before being conscious of it, or did he consecrate himself? How did his mathematical genius assert itself, how did it blossom out? Was it hard for him or easy? Did he succeed in establishing his theories and convincing his contemporaries of their importance? All these questions and many others are deeply interesting, especially for other mathematicians: if they are young, because of their dreams of the future and their hopes and doubts; if they are older, because of their memories of the past, and also, though in a different way, because of their hopes and doubts.

One soon realizes that mathematicians are much like other men, except in the single respect of their special genius, and that that genius itself has many shapes and aspects. I remember reading in John Addington Symonds's biography this portrait of a great musician:

> Here was a man Handel, a fat native of Halle, in the Duchy of Magdeburg, articled at eight years old to an organist, and from that moment given up to music—a man who never loved a woman, who (to use the words of his enthusiastic biographer) continued irritable, greedy, fond of solitude, persevering, unaffectionate, coarse and garrulous in conversation, benevolent, independent, fond of

beer, religious, without passions, and without a single intellectual taste. He had never received any education except in counterpoint. He had had no experience. Yet he could interpret the deepest psychological secrets; he could sing dithyrambs to God, or preach moral sermons; he could express the feelings of mighty nations, and speak with the voice of angels more effectually than even Milton; he could give life to passion, and in a few changes of his melody lead love through all its variations from despair to triumph—there was nothing that he did not know. The whole world had become for him music, and his chords were co-extensive with the universe. Raphael's capability to paint the school of Athens, after coming from the workshop of Perugino, was perhaps less marvellous than Handel's to delineate the length and breadth and height and depth of human nature in his choruses. We shall never comprehend, *nous autres,* the mysteries of genius. It is a God-sent clairvoyance, inexplicable, and different in kind from intellect.[5]

This account has recurred to me almost every time I have been introduced to an original scientist, for it applies to him as well as to his musical brethren.

The great mathematician may be a man of very limited experience and wisdom outside his own field and his advice in non-mathematical matters may be of very little value; he may be burdened with all kinds of passions and weaknesses; in short, he is like the rest of us except in one essential respect. When we write his biography it is clear that it is that essential thing, his genius, which must remain in the centre of the picture, but our curiosity does not stop there. We may be so deeply interested in his personality that we desire to know everything, whether good or bad, which concerns it. That is all right. Full and honest biographies should be encouraged by all means, they help us to know our fellow men and ourselves better, but that loathsome fashion of our time, which is called "debunking"—the dragging down of great men to the level of their meretricious biographers—should be discouraged. It is a matter of measure. It is very well to show all the weaknesses of a hero, but this should be subordinated to the main purpose, the description of his genius, the explanation of the discoveries which it made possible, the contemplation of the truth and beauty which it revealed.

For example, a great mathematician may be a drunkard,

for his mind's obsession with mathematical ideas may sometimes become unendurable, a real torture from which he
may wish to escape. Drink may provide a welcome relief; if
in addition his will be feeble—and there is no reason why
genius should always be associated with a will strong enough
to cope with it—and if he be afflicted with sorrows, he may
become an habitual tippler and disgrace himself accordingly.
Such facts should not be hidden by the biographer, but they
should not be unduly magnified by him. Our hero does not
become more "human" and more lovable because he is
shown to be a drunkard, though we may feel much sympathy
for him in his troubles; and, of course, his genius is not at all
explained by his drunkenness. Such a detail, we should remember, is interesting, but only in its proper place, the dim
background; to insist upon it or to focus the picture upon it
is a cruel distortion of the truth. Everybody can get drunk,
but the number of mathematicians is small, and the number
of creative mathematicians exceedingly small. It is easy
enough to cause physical intoxication, but there is no known
method for producing that kind of sacred intoxication out of
which discoveries bubble.

Mediocre people will perhaps assert that it is now too late
for discoveries, that all those of any value have already been
made. I have already disposed of this fallacy. It is safer to
assume, as a first approximation, that mathematical progress
is a function of the size of the mathematical field and of the
length of the mathematical frontiers. However, it is arguable
that the number of great mathematicians does not increase
very much from time to time, or does not continue to increase as much as one might expect. It is quite certain that
the number of original mathematicians has not increased in
proportion to the number of well trained mathematicians, or
to the availabilities for mathematical research. This confirms
my theory that mathematical theory is not very much determined by external circumstances. The main factor is the
availability of creative genius, which cannot be controlled.

In the experimental sciences, discoveries may become possible or be facilitated by the use of new instruments, and in
certain cases it is difficult to separate the virtues of the instrument from those of the observer. In mathematics, as in
music, genius can be contemplated in a greater state of
purity, and hence the history of mathematics is perhaps more
interesting to the psychologist than that of any other science.

NOTES

[1] From Mss. edited by Jules Tannery in *Bulletin des sciences mathématiques,* vol. 41, p. 260 (1906), Galois's spelling being preserved. Galois's other remarks are well worth reading; they are brilliant and inconsistent. See pages 46 and 48.

[2] See Einstein's remarks on this in *Comment je vois le monde* (Paris, 1934), pp. 173–180; cf. *Isis,* vol. 23, pp. 278–280.

[3] Ettore Bortolotti, "La propagation de la science à travers les siècles," in *Scientia,* vol. 52, supplement, pp. 133–146 (1932).

[4] Such inquisitiveness may seem idle to those relatively few men who are too engrossed in their own thoughts to care for anything else, but it represents one of the oldest human instincts. The same instinct reveals itself on a lower level through the immense curiosity concerning murders. Newspapers are skilful in pandering to such curiosity to their own profit. Even as the mass of the people are insatiable in their desire to know every detail of a murder case, so those who are more thoughtful wish to investigate every detail of scientific discoveries or other creative achievements.

[5] John Addington Symonds, as quoted by Horatio F. Brown in the latter's biography of him (London, 1895, 2 vols.), vol. 1, pp. 343–344.

ON THE SOCIOLOGY OF MATHEMATICS

D. J. STRUIK

The sociological approach to the history of mathematics has lately received increased attention. The implications of the point of view taken in the following essay, in contrast with Professor Sarton's interpretation, may not appeal to all readers. But Professor Struik is unquestionably on sound ground when he insists on the need for a sociology of mathematics. He is equally correct in insisting that mathematical discoveries, attitudes towards mathematical concepts, and methods of transmitting the mathematical heritage cannot be explained in terms of a single cause: sociological, logical, artistic and personal factors must all be carefully examined.

Some of the questions raised in this essay assume added significance in a world which appears to be dividing into two economic systems, two systems of social relationships, two types of culture. Those who believe in one of these cultures have an abiding faith in the application of the method of Dialectical Materialism to all scientific disciplines—including mathematics.

On the Sociology of Mathematics*

Defining the Problem

THE SOCIOLOGY of mathematics concerns itself with the influence of forms of social organization on the origin and growth of mathematical conceptions and methods, and the rôle of mathematics as part of the social and economic structure of a period.

The primitive forms of society, the oriental, the Graeco-Roman, the medieval feudal, the early capitalistic, the modern capitalistic and the socialist forms of society have all influenced in their various ways the acquisition of mathematical knowledge and have been in their turn subjected to its influence. There are many subsidiary problems, centering about groups in each society, all suggesting questions to be resolved. What has been the rôle of the merchant, the engineer, the surveyor, the astronomer, the navigator, the administrator, the artist, the philosopher and the professional mathematician? Why, for instance, does mathematical research flourish in one form of society, remain stagnant in another, and decay or fail to appear in a third?

Very little investigation of these problems has, as yet, been undertaken. Few persons will deny that sociological factors have influenced the development of exact sciences. Herodotus' account of the origin of geometry in the necessity of redividing the land in Egypt after the yearly inundations is a classical affirmation of this thesis. It is customary to point out that Greek rationalistic reasoning took its origin, understandably enough, in the Ionian merchant towns of Asia Minor. Leonardo Pisano's interest in the cultivation of arithmetic and algebra is always related to his professional interests as a travelled merchant. Nobody denies, in modern days, the strong connection between the expansion of electrical and aircraft industry and applied mathematics. Old and modern textbooks of trigonometry show in examples

* Reprinted from *Science and Society*, New York, vol. VI, No. 1 (Winter, 1942), pp. 58–70. By permission.

and pictures the decisive influence of astronomy, navigation and surveying on the development of the subject.

This type of correlation requires more precise definition before it is subjected to any specific analysis. Here is an example of the way in which the origin of Ionian mathematics is usually presented:

> About the seventh century B.C. an active commercial intercourse sprang up between Greece and Egypt. Naturally there arose an interchange of ideas as well as of merchandise. Greeks, thirsting for knowledge, sought the Egyptian priests for instruction. Egyptian ideas were thus transplanted across the sea and there stimulated Greek thought, directed it into new lines, and gave it a basis to work upon.[1]

This may be called a sociological approach—of a kind. But closer observation shows that it is formulated in vague generalities indicating no real sociological understanding. There had been commercial intercourse between many nations and Egypt. Why should the Greeks have formed an exception in achieving remarkable results? Travelling merchants had flourished in Egypt at least as early as 5000 B.C., and commercial intercourse can be dated back into paleolithic times. The only explanation offered is the avid "thirst for knowledge" felt by the Greeks. Whence this thirst? Not all merchants experience it. The Babylonians, upon their arrival in Sumerian lands, either as merchants or as conquerors, were sufficiently eager for knowledge to absorb the whole Sumerian science, yet no science of the Greek type resulted. They continued and improved the ancient methods. The difference in the case of the Greeks must be explained by more penetrating methods than a reference to mercantile activity and a thirst for knowledge. The sociologist can contribute materially by showing in which way Greek society differed radically from all previous and all later forms of social structure. Something entirely new must have occurred, and an attempt must therefore be made to define it, first in social terms, and then in terms of scientific thought.

The rise of mathematics in ancient Ionia presents, then, the following problem. How is it possible that a group of Greeks, mainly of mercantile class, not only became interested in the science of the ancient Orient, but approached it from an entirely original point of view? And furthermore, how is it possible that only some of the problems raised by these Ionians received full, if onesided, attention, and others remained dormant until modern times?

The merchant has had an influence on mathematics, but only on certain parts of it. He is interested in computation and needs a sound elementary arithmetic. If he is a travelling man, his interests go out toward some geometry sufficient for geography and the knowledge of the motion of sun and stars. His wit is sharpened by competition and the possibility of individual profit, although this may not always lead to the search for profounder truth in mathematics. Sometimes he may help science by playing the Maecenas. To establish the existence of mercantile relations is not of itself sufficient to prove the assured growth of mathematics beyond a certain elementary level.[2]

The institution of slavery poses a similar problem in causation. There is a widely accepted theory that the nature of Graeco-Roman society, and with it that of its peculiar type of science, was determined chiefly by its slave character. The decay of the system of slavery is thus made a main factor in the decline of science. There is a reasonable foundation for this theory, but it must be thoroughly qualified. Ancient oriental society also knew slavery, but its science had an entirely different character from that of Greece and Rome. Its slavery showed little decline and the political and cultural expansion, contraction and stagnation of the oriental forms of society did not necessarily correspond with developments in slavery or in science. A primary distinction is to be made between Graeco-Roman slavery for production and oriental slavery for luxury or for public works.[3] A second distinction is that slavery in Greece was to be found mainly in industry, and Roman slavery not only in industry, but in agriculture as well. We submit that further analysis of these forms of slavery and their development can yield a new understanding of the scientific advances and limitations of each period, and of the relative place in the history of science of men like Ahmes, the scribe of the Egyptian Papyrus Rhind; Euclid, the Alexandrinian of the early period; Plotinus, the Neoplatonist; or Alkhwarizmi, the Mohammedan algebrist. We must lean here on work already done, mostly in related fields, by men like Farrington and Winspear for Graeco-Roman antiquity, and Wittfogel for the ancient Orient.[4]

We should not, on the other hand, stretch our sociological analysis too far, and forget a very obvious thing: namely, that a scientific process often follows the courses suggested by its internal logical structure, the frame built by results already obtained. The student writes his thesis because the professor wants him to clear up an obscure point in his own work. We are likely to find such a situation often within a relatively stable social and cultural frame. An example is furnished by ancient Egyptian, Babylonian and Chinese mathematics, once its pattern was well established. Here we find, sometimes for many centuries, actual stagnation, and when progress is made it is obtained by discoveries directly dependent on the previously existing knowledge and technique. Another example is the development of algebra in sixteenth century Italy. After Tartaglia and Cardan, working as direct pupils of certain Bolognese professors, had solved the third degree equation before an admiring public, Cardan's pupil, Ferrari, showed in 1545 how to solve the biquadratic equation. This is an example of the discovery of an objective relation, the mathematical kinship of two kinds of equations, inside the framwork of a particular social structure. The continuity of this structure allowed the further discovery of more related mathematical relations. In Cardan's work a real number had appeared as the sum of two complex ("sophistical") numbers. This led the Bolognese professor Bombelli to the publication, in 1572, of a systematic investigation of the algebra of imaginaries. The history of mathematics, as described in our usual textbooks, concentrates on just such discoveries, tracing the discovery of new results almost exclusively to internal logical development with relative neglect of sociological factors. Yet, even in cases where the purely mathematical factor is dominant, sociological factors do exist. They are apparent in the purely social fact that talented men of the time go in for mathematics, are encouraged to teach, to publish and to foster disciples. In other periods, there may be as many men of talent, but their genius is led into other channels, some of which we now consider as sidetracks.[5]

Conditions for the Operation of Sociological Factors

In periods of profound social upheaval, of transition, or in periods in which peoples learn from other peoples of a widely varied social and cultural background, the sociologi-

cal factor may give the most important clue to the understanding of the changes in mathematical knowledge. It is a
matter of record that the fundamental change in Chinese
mathematics from the oriental stage into western technique
and scholarship was due to the Jesuit missionaries who entered China in the sixteenth century on the wave of European capitalist expansion. Let us pass to a case where the
sociological factors have not so well been established. The
so-called Hindu-Arabic number system, a decimal position
system with ten tokens, including a token for zero, was introduced into Mesopotamia, probably from India, in the
time of the Sassanian kings, perhaps in the seventh century.[6]
In the thirteenth century and later it penetrated into Europe
and thus it became our present number system. The old explanation for its success was rather simple. It assumed that
the intrinsic superiority of this system eventually impressed
itself by its own weight upon practical minds to such an extent that all other number systems were discarded. It is true
that the Hindu-Arabic system is far superior to the Roman
system or to the ancient abacus. Less convincing is the argument that it was superior to the system used by the Greeks.
This system, with twenty-seven tokens, taken from the alphabet, had no position method and no token for zero, and seems
at first to us rather cumbersome. It loses much of its clumsi-
ness, however, for anyone who has ever tried it. After a little
practice, it is seen that this system is as easy for the purpose
of elementary arithmetic, inclusive of fractions, as the Hindu-
Arabic system.[7] For a merchant or a surveyor of the Near
Orient it made little difference whether he used the Hindu
or the Greek system.[8] We conclude that there must have been
extra-mathematical reasons for the victory of one system over
the other. There are several indications that such reasons may
actually be found in the history of Sassanian and Abbasid
times, when there was widespread prejudice among the orien-
tals against everything, a hatred based on a difference in economic position. Our first extant reference to the ten Hindu
numerals outside of India is found in the writings of Bishop
Severus Sebokht (662 A.D.), who mentions these numerals
for the express purpose of showing that the Greeks did not
have a monopoly of culture.[9] There existed under the early
Abbasid khalifs in Bagdad a mathematical school which
seems to have refused intentionally to accept lessons from
the Greeks and turned for inspiration to the ancient Jewish

and Babylonian sources.[10] To this school belonged
Alkhwarizmi, the father of our algebra. This hatred of Greek
influence and domination was one of the chief causes for the
easy victories gained by the rising Islam in Syria.[11]

We find it again easy to understand that the Hindu-Arabic
system gained a victory over the abacus and the Roman
numerals among the rising European merchant class of the
thirteenth and sixteenth centuries. It was indeed technically
superior. It is, however, often forgotten that the ancient
Greek system was still in existence, used in influential Constantinople and certainly known to the Venetians, who were
masters of Constantinople from 1203 to 1261. Why then did
the Italian merchants select the Arabic system? The answer
to this question does not seem to have been given, but some
facts may be suggestive. "Arabic civilization was tangible
enough in Sicily and Spain, not only in the Moorish part of
it, but in places like Toledo, which were again in Christian
hands; the Arabic speaking people encircled the Mediter-
ranean Sea and dominated the Asiatic trade."[12] The Arabic
system seems to have appeared in Italy first in Florence and
Pisa, which had closer connections with the Arabic world
than with the Greek and which were in endless commercial
rivalry with Venice.[13]

In present-day society technology influences the development of mathematics either directly, by placing technical
problems capable of mathematical treatment before the expert, or indirectly through physics, chemistry and other natural sciences. An attempt has been made to discriminate between "applied" and "pure" mathematics, the "applied" part
being directly related to technology, and thus showing more
clearly its social background. This distinction, which only
dates back to the nineteenth century, becomes every year less
popular with the gradual discovery of the elementary dialectical law that all applied mathematics may as well be pure,
and all pure mathematics may be applied. Even the "purest"
type of mathematics is not without its sociological stain.
Modern aircraft design, communication engineering, the new
work in plasticity, and many other fields of engineering require extremely refined mathematical tools which are only
partly discussed in our purely theoretical texts. Fields such
as harmonic analysis, tensor calculus, real and complex integration, group theory, mostly developed without any special

relation to technological applicability, turn out to be abstractions of some very concrete relationships in nature and useful guides for control of industry. I believe that modern mathematicians generally discover the social background of their science rather through these conscious relations to technology than through a study of history.[14]

It is, however, important to notice that this fundamental rôle of technology is typical only for modern industrial society. It was almost entirely unknown in the ancient Orient and in Graeco-Roman society. There was some indirect influence through navigation and architecture, but we do not hear of the mathematical computation of a technical structure until capitalist times (with some exceptions, as some of Archimedes' structures). We have no evidence that the huge technical works of the Chinese, the Babylonians, the Romans required more than the most elementary type of mathematics. There certainly was an influence of technology on exact science, as testified by the many writers on mechanics, but the application never got beyond elementary beginnings. Vitruvius, in his *Architecture,* pays high tribute to mathematics, but theory and practice are divorced. His eighth book describes practical means to convey water to houses and cities, deals with leaden pipes, earthen tubes and channels, and can be read without any mathematical training. His ninth book deals with methods of doubling the area of a square, the theorem of Pythagoras, Archimedes' law of hydrostatics and the duplication of a cube, but seems to be without much bearing on architecture. The names of inventors and technicians of antiquity (Ctesibios, Philon, Frontinus) have no place or hardly a place in the history of mathematics, not even for their indirect influence, the only important exception being Archimedes and perhaps also Heron.

With the advent of modern capitalism, technology begins to play an important part in the development of mathematics. The development of mechanical appliances in Renaissance times is, as H. Grossmann has analyzed, the immediate source of modern mechanics as a science.[15] Mechanics now advanced beyond the narrow limits of antiquity and became the source of inspiration for the mathematicians. In this first stage it inspired the philosophers and led to their belief in the mathematical structure of the universe. Many mathematicians were inventors themselves, as Descartes, Pascal,

Newton and Leibniz. For Leibniz, the study of exact science was part of his search for the general method of invention and discovery.

Application of the new tools to problems of technology came only gradually. In the eighteenth century, Euler and the Bernoullis applied their mathematics to ship and canal building. Most influence of technology remained indirect, even after the Industrial Revolution, through the intermediary rôle of mechanics and physics. The present direct influence of technology on mathematics begins in the twentieth century with the whole transformation of the rôle of science in industry.

From this brief sketch we may conclude that a study of the influence of technology on mathematics might be very instructive. One thing stands out. The technological foundation of a form of society, its buildings, aqueducts, tools, ships, its inventive genius, its technical skill, is not of itself an indicator of the size and the tendencies of the mathematics cultivated in this society. There may be influence, of the one upon the other, but this influence may differ in quantity and in quality. We must see the technological structure of a society not as an isolated thing, but in its full relationship with many other aspects of the society such as the existence of slavery, the extent of mercantile intercourse, the influence of class struggles, the stability of the social forms and the amount of leisure.

A startling series of new conceptions is hardly ever the result of a development of mathematical ideas in isolated independence. Sociological factors play some sort of rôle, it is clear. Yet new scientific conceptions need not be born in the very midst of struggles, but perhaps rather on the periphery. The stimuli operating for advancement take effect slowly and require, not only a certain maturity, but also quietude. There are some obvious exceptions like the case of Thales, the legendary father of Greek mathematics, who is supposed to have been himself a militant member of his class. Descartes enlisted in the Dutch army, at that time one of the spearheads of the bourgeois revolution, and participated in the Thirty Years' War, but soon discovered that most great ideas are born in quietude. Galois, the young French genius of two centuries later, participated actively in the July revolution, and soon afterwards found his death. More typical is the original work done by men in peaceful settings, not too far away from the centers of social economic activity, like Newton at Cambridge, Euler at Berlin or Poincaré at Paris. The first mathematical research institute was founded, not in Athens with its sharp class struggles, but in Alexandria where economic activity was carried on in relatively peaceful surroundings. Sometimes the geographical distance between social activity and mathematical inventiveness becomes very large, the most extreme case being the discovery of non-Euclidean geometries in Hungary and in Russia during the early decades of the nineteenth century. Both discoveries were inspired by the genius of Gauss, who himself led an uneventful life in a provincial town of semi-feudal Germany. It would be a great mistake, however, to see in these remarkable cases of semi-detachment of social progress and scientific activity a proof of the independence of mathematical invention. Gauss belongs, with Lessing before him and with his older contemporary Goethe, to the great German awakening of the late eighteenth and the early nineteenth century, which Franz Mehring has traced to its bourgeois roots.[16] The relation of Gauss' work to that of the mathematicians of revolutionary France is intimate to such an extent that Felix Klein has drawn up a long comparative table between the achievements of Gauss and those of Legendre, one of the French mathematicians in whom we can study the influence of the French Revolution on the development of mathematics. Gauss, compared to Legendre, always dug deeper, but Göttingen gave more leisure than Paris.[17] Working on ideas which would dominate modern mathematics, Gauss remained in person rather the type of the eighteenth century.

Mathematics in Relation to Other Disciplines

Felix Klein, in comparing great mathematicians of the nineteenth century, has remarked that creative mathematicians may have very different outlooks on life, and yet little of their particular outlook appears in their work.[18] He came to this conclusion by comparing the work of Catholics like Weierstrass and Cauchy, Protestants like Riemann, and Jews like Jacobi, and in the relatively small period with which he deals and the relatively small range of religious views, his statement is not incorrect. It constitutes a warning to us when we try to generalize. Philosophies and religions reflect certain objective social relationships, perhaps those of a bygone age, and as such may carry elements stimulating or discouraging

Fitz Memorial Library 30082

Endicott Junior College

to mathematical work. In Greek society, mathematics was born and fostered in the sharpest clash of philosophies. Materialists and idealists struggled for the interpretation of mathematical conceptions. The first clear statements of the problems of the infinitesimal came from Zeno of Elea in an attempt to harass either the Pythagoreans or the Atomists. When the dust of the battlefields cleared, the strategic mathematical positions were held by the idealist philosophers of the Platonic school with their emphasis on logical structure and sterility of application.[19] Euclid, who was in the Platonic tradition, embodied this point of view in his "Elements." In so far as these "Elements" still form, in essence and in spirit, the backbone of our ordinary plane and solid geometry, Plato's influence is still felt in our present-day instruction. The ordinary type of American high school texts on geometry combines a maximum of logical structure with a minimum of applications to modern science and to modern life. Here the obstinate persistence of a certain type of mathematics in instruction goes back to social and cultural conditions of long ago.

Another example of a philosophical school which profoundly influenced mathematical creation is the materialism of Descartes and his followers, on which we have already touched before. One of the main tenets of this school was the mathematical nature of the universe and the view of mathematics as the key to the control of nature. This creed was shared by many men who could not follow the Cartesians in their materialism, like Leibniz, and it accounts for the popularity of mathematics in progressive circles of the seventeenth and eighteenth centuries. And, to give an example of recent times, dialectical materialism, far more than any of the past philosophies, has acted as a stimulant on the study of the exact sciences in the U.S.S.R., flourishing under the impact of socialist construction.

There are also cases of philosophical attitudes which have discouraged the study of mathematics. The gradual decay of Roman slave society focused the attention of many logically trained minds on the salvation of the soul rather than on questions concerning control of number and space. This explains why the Church Fathers, with all their intellectual endowment, devoted their attention to dialectical exercises of a theological kind, neglecting natural science and mathematics. All the well-known mathematicians of this period, from

Ptolemy to Proclus, were heathen, and one of them, Hypatia, died an anti-Christian martyr. They hardly contributed new results, and some of them, like Proclus, concentrated also on ethical problems.

We may go nearer home to see the effects of a philosophy, of perhaps simply a mental attitude, on the pursuit of mathematical studies. Whence the pride among so many high school and college graduates that mathematics means absolutely nothing to them? Whence, at the same time, the timid wish among some others that they might know more about it, in the way of Henry Adams?[20] How is it that even among cultured men and women of our age, there is a firm belief that mathematics is fixed, finished for all time, and the mathematician a repeater of the lore of the past? This attitude of mind is destructive for further progress of exact science as a tool for social reconstruction. Its roots must be determined by a study of the rôle of mathematics in modern society as a whole, not only in its schools or industries.

These widely sundered instances will suffice to show that there is room for a sociology of mathematics. They also show that a careful analysis of the nature of social structures is needed before an attempt is made to interpret its influence on the status of exact science. Superficiality only engenders disappointment and makes such work look ludicrous. The tremendous advances in economic history, during the last decades, have made the task at any rate potentially possible. The history of technology, also an important factor in a sociological approach, as we have seen, is nevertheless still in a rather unsatisfactory state.[21] The lack can be made good without too much difficulty with the abundant documentation at our disposal. Fortunately the periods in which the mathematician is interested are usually also the periods most keenly studied by others—the civilizations of China, Babylonia, ancient Egypt, classical Greece, the Roman Empire, Europe under feudalism and after its disintegration, and modern capitalism. An exception seems to be the early world of Islam, and India before the Mohammedans, concerning which sociological information is extremely unsatisfactory.

We finish with a final warning. We should always be aware that a mathematical discovery, a state of mind regarding mathematics, a system of teaching is never explained by one cause alone. Life is complex and even the most modest and the most subtle act reflects in some way or another an infinity of aspects of the real world. We cannot say that one particular factor was responsible for a particular occurrence or mental state. We must discover the way all factors—sociological, logical, artistic, and personal—have played a rôle in the case under investigation, never forgetting, however, that man is a social being even when he worries about the straight lines on hypercones in seven dimensional space.

NOTES

[1] F. Cajori, *History of Mathematics* (2nd ed., New York, 1930), p. 15.

[2] This is borne out by books which point out the influence of the merchant on mathematics, as D. E. Smith, *History of Mathematics*, 2 vols. (Boston, 1923), where even on an elementary level the stimulating influence of other factors is taken into account, notably that of astronomy. See for the influence of the merchant: D. E. Smith, "Mathematical Problems in Relation to the History of Economics and Commerce," *American Mathematical Monthly*, xxiv (1917), pp. 221–223, or W. Sombart, *Der Bourgeois* (München-Leipzig, 1920), pp. 164–169.

[3] E. Meyer, "Sklaverei im Altertum" (1898), in *Kleine Schriften* (1910), pp. 189–190; also K. Wittfogel, *Wirtschaft und Gesellschaft Chinas*, 1 (Leipzig, 1931), p. 393; "Die Theorie der orientalischen Gesellschaft," *Zeitschr. für Sozialforschung*, vii (1930), p. 96.

[4] B. Farrington, "Vesalius on the Ruin of Ancient Medicine," *The Modern Quarterly* (1938), pp. 23–28; A Winspear, *The Genesis of Plato's Thought* (New York, 1940), p. 348; K. Wittfogel, *l.c.*

[5] "There were perhaps as many men of genius in the Middle Ages as now; at least, my survey gives that impression, which would be confirmed, I am sure, by statistical inquiry. If these medieval scientists did not make a good showing, we may ask what men like Gauss, Faraday or Claude Bernard would have done if they had been born in the eighth or ninth century." G. Sarton, *Introduction to the History of Science*, 1 (Baltimore, 1927), p. 20.

[6] The data are still incomplete. This number system, according to some investigators, may well have been known to Alexandrian Greeks. See D. E. Smith and L. Karpinski, *Hindu-Arabic Numerals* (Boston, London, 1911), and F. Cajori, *l.c.*, pp. 88–90. It became widely used after the eighth century under the Arabs.

[7] This has been observed, *e.g.* by J. G. Smyly, "The Employment of the Alphabet in Greek Logistics," *Recueil offert à J. Nicole* (Genève, 1905), pp. 515–530, who defends his thesis against the older point of view of Hankel, Gow and Cantor. See also T. L. Heath, *A Manual of Greek Mathematics* (Oxford, 1931), pp. 28

and 31, who calls the Greek system for elementary operations "little less convenient than ours."

[8] In order to appreciate the value of the Greek system, we must keep in mind that the arithmetical meaning of the Greek letters was as familiar to the Greeks as the meaning of 0, 1, 2, etc. is to us.

[9] The reference in D. E. Smith, *History of Mathematics*, 1, pp. 166–167.

[10] See S. Gandz, "The Mishnat ha Middot, the First Hebrew Geometry of about 150 C.E. and the Geometry of Muhammed ibn Musa Al-Khowarizmi," *Quellen und Studien zur Geschichte der Mathematik A* 2 (1936).

[11] P. K. Hitti, *History of the Arabs* (London, 1937), p. 153.

[12] G. Sarton, *Introduction to the History of Science*, II (Baltimore, 1931), p. 6.

[13] There were also other numerical tokens in use, of yet dubious origins. See G. Falco, "Un indovinello paleografico," *Bolletino Storico-bibliografico Subalpino,* xxxvii (1935).

[14] See T. C. Fry, "Industrial Mathematics," in *Research—A National Resource,* 11 (Dec., 1940), Report of the National Research Council to the National Research Planning Board (Washington, 1941), pp. 268–288. Dr. Fry quotes a stimulating remark of Dr. H. M. Evjen: "Higher mathematics, of course, means simply those branches of the science which have not as yet found a wide field of application and hence have not as yet, so to speak, emerged from obscurity. It is therefore a temporal and subjective term" (p. 273). The remark is of interest as an oversimplification of the sociological approach.

[15] H. Grossmann, "Die gesellschaftlichen Grundlagen der mechanistischen Philosophie und die Manufaktur," *Zeitschr. für Sozialforschung,* IV (1935), pp. 161–231.

[16] For instance in *Die Lessing-Legende* (4e Aufl., Stuttgart, 1913).

[17] Felix Klein, *Vorlesungen über die Entwicklung der Mathematik im 19. Jahrhundert,* 1 (Berlin, 1926), pp. 60–61.

[18] *Ibid.,* p. 71: "This short survey affirms the experience of every study of man, namely that in questions of *Weltanschauung* the gifts of the intellect are not decisive. The disposition of heart and will, the influences of education, the experiences, the whole impact of the exterior world and of one's own nature are active in its formulation." Again: "There is often an opinion prevailing among the public that mathematicians and natural scientists must have a tendency for liberal, and even radical opinions, in accordance with their unprejudiced logically keen way of thinking. One look at history teaches that this opinion is not at all in agreement with the facts. Our science has outstanding representatives in all camps and parties."

[19] For the interpretation of Zeno's statements see F. Cajori,

"The History of Zeno's Arguments on Motion," *American Mathematical Monthly*, xxii (1915). A guide to the understanding of the social meaning of mathematics in ancient Greece is Winspear, *op. cit.*, and M. A. Dinnik, *Outline of the History of Philosophy of Classical Greece* (Moscow, 1936, in Russian). We disagree, however, with Winspear's interpretation of Zeno's paradoxes as mere sophistry; they were remarkable documents of mathematical philosophy, and as such their constructive influence has been enormous.

[20] "At best he would never have been a mathematician; at worst he would never have cared to be one; but he needed to read mathematics, like any other universal language, and he never reached the alphabet," *The Education of Henry Adams* (Boston: Houghton Mifflin, 1927), p. 60. See also p. 449. Henry Adams' yearning has the flavor of a bygone century—in agreement with the whole character he gives himself throughout.

[21] One of the first writers to point out the crucial significance of a historical study of technology was Marx, see *Capital* 1 (Modern Library ed.), ch. 25, section 1, p. 406.

AN INTRODUCTION TO
MODERN MATHEMATICAL THOUGHT

CARROLL V. NEWSOM

The phrase modern mathematics, *generally speaking, refers to those aspects of mathematics which are created and characterized by the axiomatic method. Although adumbrated by classical Greek logicians and geometers, contemporary axiomatics did not appear upon the scene until shortly after the middle of the nineteenth century, heralded by the invention of non-Euclidean geometry. By the turn of the century (1898–1910), due chiefly to the work of Hilbert, Brouwer, Whitehead and Russell, the foundations of modern mathematics had emerged full-blown.*

In the present excerpt from the early writings of Professor Newsom, the flavor of the "foundations" has been faithfully portrayed. Originally comprising a series of lectures for students, in its present condensed form Professor Newsom's essay is still a delightful introduction to the nature of contemporary mathematical thought.

An Introduction to Modern Mathematical Thought *

Forerunners of Mathematical Systems

ONE FREQUENTLY hears that mathematics is static. There could be no greater misconception. Without doubt there have been long periods of time when mathematics was virtually a static art. Creative possibilities were not recognized. But we are now living in the greatest age of all time from the standpoint of mathematical development. This is due, in part, to a better comprehension of the nature of mathematics.

One must realize that the decision as to what is mathematics or what is not mathematics is, to a great extent, arbitrary. Hence not all mathematicians agree. Bertrand Russell[1] has defined mathematics as the "class of all propositions of the type 'p implies q.'" It seems desirable in this study to describe a mathematical system as the resultant of two components, namely, a set of axioms and a system of logic. Mathematics, then, is the totality of such mathematical systems. Although this bears some resemblance to the definition promulgated by Russell, it may prove somewhat more acceptable here. The construction involved as the two components mentioned above are combined is frequently characterized as the mathematical method of analysis.

The beginning of any mathematical system lies in the postulational technique. To indicate the necessary emphasis upon the postulates the mathematical method is frequently known as the postulational or the axiomatic method. Hence, it seems appropriate to consider at once the first component involved in a mathematical system, namely, the axioms. In this connection it may be observed that the modern mathematician no longer distinguishes between postulates and axioms. Such words as axiom, postulate, and assumption are usually used synonymously.

Probably Aristotle (384–322 B.C.) was the first person to give serious consideration to the nature of axioms. It must be

* Reprinted in revised and condensed form, with the approval of Professor C. V. Newsom, and by permission of the University of New Mexico Press; from the University of New Mexico Bulletin, Philosophical Series, Vol. 1, No. 2, Oct. 1, 1936.

admitted, however, that probably his study was influenced tremendously by the previous work of Plato. The logician looks to Aristotle as the father of the science of logic. Aristotle's original system of logic was undoubtedly framed upon models taken from mathematics; but the mathematician has been inclined to ignore the important work of Aristotle upon the study of axioms and his other contributions to deductive science. In 1904, Heiberg[2] made a most valuable collection of mathematical extracts from Aristotle. These quotations indicate that Aristotle had a rather modern view of the fundamental nature of mathematical knowledge.

The most famous of all mathematical systems was organized by Euclid shortly after the time of Aristotle. Euclid was the first professor of mathematics in the famous university of Alexandria. Hence, his period of activity may be dated approximately at 300 B.C. Virtually nothing is known of Euclid. Probably he was a Greek rather than an Egyptian. Certainly, however, he may be characterized as the first great mathematical organizer. His monumental work, "The Elements," in thirteen books, is known to every school boy. Practically all of the geometrical material in modern plane and solid geometry texts is contained in parts of six of the books (1, 3, 4, 6, 11, and 12) of "The Elements." How much of this material was original with Euclid remains a question. Undoubtedly he had before him the already famous geometrical text-book written by Theudius of Magnesia. Moreover, he probably was influenced in his scheme of organization by the ideas of various pupils of Aristotle and of Plato. Certainly his organization with an explicit statement of his definitions and of his axioms at the very start of his analysis was a landmark in the history of mathematical thought. This is true in spite of the fact that the definitions and axioms would not meet modern requirements of rigor.

The first part of the nineteenth century furnished the second great landmark in the history of the axiomatic method. The era of Bolyai and Lobachevsky really marked the dawn of modern mathematical thinking. The invention of non-Euclidean geometry by these two men, independent of each other, marked the first turning away from the dominance of Euclid. A foundation for their work had been laid by Saccheri, Gauss, and others; but when, at the age of twenty-one, Bolyai wrote to his father saying, "I have created a new universe from nothing," one period had been finished and a new one had begun.

The only real difference between the geometry of Euclid and the geometry invented by Bolyai and Lobachevsky is that the parallel postulate of Euclid is replaced by another assumption. One might consider that the two inventors looked upon the matter as a sporting proposition to see what type of theorems would result if such a replacement were made. Certainly, as a result of the particular change which the two men both made, a strange geometry resulted. Those theorems of Euclid that were independent of postulate 5 still held in the new geometry. Other theorems in the old geometry were replaced by such amazing conclusions as this: that in a plane, instead of one line, two lines could be drawn through a point parallel to a given line and that through this point an infinite number of lines might be drawn lying in the angle between the first two and such that no one of the infinity of lines would intersect the given line.

Riemann demonstrated still another geometry in 1854 at Göttingen. Replacing the parallel postulate by still another assumption, he obtained a geometry in which all lines were of finite length and the sum of the angles of a triangle was greater than two right angles.

To the novice such conclusions seem strange and probably ridiculous. To the mathematician the results were extremely important. The thought that the axioms underlying a mathematical system must be "obvious truths" slowly became a thing of the past. It no longer is demanded that the postulates or the resulting theorems should appeal to a person's notion of truth. Some of the axioms may seem to be true, some may seem to be false, while others may be indeterminate in the sense that they do not possess the property of truth or falsity; yet the resulting system is accepted as a mathematical system if it is logically consistent. In fact, *consistency*, not truth, is the key word to mathematical thought. Although there are certain properties which a good set of axioms should possess, yet the axioms are to a great extent merely arbitrary starting statements.

During the past century higher and higher standards have been required of postulational technique. The systematic study of the problem probably originated with Peano in 1889. In the United States important contributions were made by E. H. Moore and his followers, and by others during the early part of the twentieth century. However, the most influential work was the course of lectures given by Hilbert upon Euclidean geometry at the University of Göttingen during the winter semester of 1898–99, and which was subsequently published.

During recent years there has been a most interesting tendency to develop new mathematical systems. Virtually the only requirement for a new mathematical system is a new set of axioms; and, since the set of axioms is to great extent arbitrary, one aspect of recent mathematical activities is easily understood.

Many features of modern mathematics that may seem strange to the novice may be understood if one appreciates the use to which a set of axioms may be put. Frequently the mathematician is asked, "How can there be so many different kinds of space?" or "How can there be more than three dimensions?" It is essential again to recall that the mathematician is not interested in reality as the term is usually understood. Hence, he can have any kind of space or any kind of dimensional theory by the simple process of setting up the proper set of axioms. Naturally, it is difficult for the mathematician to limit his attention to mathematical systems of the traditional type. Moreover, the modern definition of mathematics does not require that mathematical systems be restricted to those involving such words as line, space, or number.

The Nature of Axioms

Mathematics has gone even further in the consideration of certain fundamental aspects of axioms. As yet in this study no attention has been paid to the language of the axioms. Technically, of course, such a consideration should come first in any discussion such as this. Some parts of speech have not caused the mathematician any concern. For example, he looks upon articles as non-essentials. They have been introduced for rhetorical and literary nicety. Other parts of speech have given him great concern. Especially has the matter of definition of words caused many a mathematician to stay awake at night. The mathematician does not intend to indulge in the fallacy of the dictionary. A dictionary will define word, *A*, in terms of word *B*. Word, *B*, will be defined in terms of word, *C*, etc. Soon it may be observed that a word in the sequence will be defined in terms of word, A. Hence, ultimately word, A, is defined in terms of word, A. Such a process is justified, of course, for dictionary purposes, since the hope exists that somewhere in the sequence of words a word will be found which possesses meaning to the user of the dictionary. Thus word, A, can be interpreted. Such vicious circle analysis is not desirable in mathematics. In fact, mathematicians have come to the conclusion that certain fundamental words in any science must be left undefined. This may seem unfortunate but apparently no other course is open to us. This is less of a difficulty in mathematics than in other fields of thought probably since ultimately meaning is subtracted from a pure mathematical system. It is considered desirable in any mathematical system to reduce the number of undefined words to a minimum. There has been much study of this particular point. For example, it has been found that in Euclidean geometry it is possible to reduce the number of undefined terms to three. In other words, one can define all other necessary terms by starting with the set of undefined words: point, line, and congruent. An alternate set of words which gives equal success is the collection: point, between, and congruent. Of course, if certain fundamental words are undefined, it follows that other words, which are defined in terms of them, are likewise devoid of any fundamental meaning. It is not surprising, then, that Bertrand Russell said, "Mathematics is the subject in which we never know what we are talking about, nor whether what we say is true."

As implied above, however, the concept of definition does have its place in mathematics. When it seems to be desirable to extend the vocabulary beyond the primitive words, new words may be introduced. However, such new words must be defined in terms of the primitive words. The precise manner in which the new words are to be related to the undefined words through the medium of the definition is still a matter of controversy. Frequently the addition of new words to the vocabulary of a mathematical system is used in most interesting fashion. Whenever a system does not give much promise for further extension and the worker upon that system has exhausted the necessary research to enable him to keep in good standing with his profession, the insertion of a new word will give him a new thing to play with. It may be possible to prove a tremendous number of new theorems about the new word.

Not only is a consideration of the language of an axiom important but the form of such a primitive statement is likewise a matter of concern. By common agreement the form is that of a logical proposition, that is, a statement in which something is affirmed or denied of a subject. However, at once a difficulty is encountered. The statement, "Two points determine a line," is a rather common axiom in geometry. The statement appears to involve an affirmation. But it must be recalled that the words, point and line, are undefined words; hence, they are without meaning. The geometer may be picturing a very small dot for his point and a narrow mark for his line; thus he may nod in approval when the axiom is quoted. Another person may think of a pin point for his point and a clothes line for his line; thus he may think the statement sounds very ridiculous. Either person has a right to his own interpretation of the words involved. The fact is that such a statement as the axiom quoted above may be either true or false according to the content given to the undefined words. As it stands, however, since the words do not possess content, we can not say that it is either true or false. So the statement is not an actual proposition; rather it is merely in the form of a proposition. The novice in mathematics may be considerably disturbed by the lack of content in his words. Many words used by mathematicians already possess some sort of a meaning to many people. For such people it probably is desirable to replace the words by symbols of a new type. For example, a common axiom might be written, "X is a Y." Certainly that sentence is in the form of a proposition but a person is not tempted to ascribe to it any properties of truth or falsity.

As the mathematician observes the statement, "X is a Y," he is at once reminded of the concept of function in mathematics. Although the function theory expert would not agree completely, it may be stated that a variable is a function of one or more other variables if the first or dependent variable depends upon the other or independent variables in such a way that when the independent variables are given, the dependent variable may be determined.

It may be observed, therefore, that an axiom written in the accepted form has the form of a proposition and the characteristics of a mathematical function. Hence, an axiom is said to be a typical propositional function. Frege used propositional functions in his work, but Bertrand Russell receives the credit for the real development of the idea. It might be interesting to read what Russell had to say in regard to the concept. He defined a propositional function thus: "A propositional function is simply an expression containing an undetermined constituent, or several undetermined constituents, and becoming a proposition as soon as the undetermined constituents are determined. If I say 'x is a man' or 'n is a number' that is a propositional function."[3]

It may be remarked, at this time, that the axioms are not the only propositional functions in a mathematical system. The statements, which are deduced logically from the axioms, are likewise, of necessity, propositional functions.

Mathematicians believe that the notion of propositional function is a very important one. It is almost strange that the thought is so recent. Perhaps many so-called propositions are in reality propositional functions. C. J. Keyser has expressed an interesting thought in the statement: "That fact goes far to account for the endless disputations of men. For what can be a more prolific source of wasteful controversy than propositional functions uttered as propositions and regarded by mankind as propositions and thus believed to be true or false though in fact they are neither true or false?"[4]

Ideal Requirements of a Set of Axioms

So far the discussion has had to do with individual axioms and their properties. Mathematics has gone still further and has set up a group of requirements pertaining to the whole set of axioms which form the background of a mathematical system. These requirements are *consistency*, *independence*, and *categoricalness*.

The notion of consistency in a set of mathematical axioms is simple if one is willing to treat the matter superficially. If, however, an individual desires to study the question seriously, he will find that there is no problem more abstract or difficult. Moreover, it must be understood that some of the greatest of modern mathematical thinkers are at present delving deeply into this topic.

A set of axioms may be spoken of as being consistent if it is impossible to deduce contradictory theorems from them. Of course, if contradictory theorems are obtained as a logical consequence of the axioms, the indication is that there exists contradiction within the axioms themselves. This concept would not be particularly difficult if it were not for the fact that mathematics makes use of a certain amount of logical terminology which probably needs some restrictions. This fact is appreciated acutely by the mathematician as he studies some of the modern logical paradoxes. A typical one might be interesting.

Probably one of the simplest as well as one of the best known of the logical paradoxes is the Russell paradox. It involves the word, class, which is one of the primitive terms of logic. However, it may be considered to be a word synonymous with such words as collection or aggregate. This must not be thought of as a definition, however. The paradox, then, has to do with what will be known as an ordinary class. Any class which does not contain itself as an element is said to be such a class. As an illustration of this it may be said that the word, French, represents an ordinary class since the class of all words denoted by "French" does not contain the word, French. The word, English, is not ordinary, since the word, English, is contained in the class of words known as "English." The problem, then, is to consider the class, C, of all ordinary classes. Is such a class an ordinary class or a not-ordinary class? One will observe with a little thought that the assumption of either possibility leads to contradiction. It is impossible to tell, in other words, whether class C is ordinary or not-ordinary. Such a state of affairs is very sad indeed and individual mathematicians and logicians do not agree upon the remedy. The problem does involve the mathematical notion of infinity. Perhaps such a concept should be restricted or perhaps the word, class, needs some limitations. Suffice it to say, the idea of contradiction is not as simple as it may first seem to be.

Hilbert and his followers have been working for several years in an attempt to prove the whole of pure mathematics consistent. The effort involves the juggling of tremendous symbolic systems and many feel that there is little probability of success. Certainly they must be discouraged and mathematicians in general are disturbed by the recent finding of K. Gödel of Vienna. About 1931 he showed, when phrased roughly in popular language, that a definite contradiction can be deduced from any proof which professes to prove the impossibility of the occurrence of contradiction in mathematics; that is, any attempt to demonstrate consistency in mathematics will lead in itself to inconsistency. As yet, no refutation of his findings has been brought forward. This result is important not only for mathematics, but for the whole of science.

Even if it be admitted that there exists no completely rigorous test for the consistency of a set of axioms, yet any mathematician desires to indulge in some form of check for the set which he may have created. The common method is to give a concrete representation of the system, in which the undefined terms are given content, and for which the axioms are all satisfied. If, then, the mathematician is able to picture a real or ideal situation (Is there any difference?) in which all of the axioms which now have value are represented in non-contradictory fashion, he reasons that there is no contradiction involved. This will be seen to be true if one considers that if any contradiction might arise in the original mathematical system a contradiction which corresponds to it would be observed in the material or ideal representation. It must be observed that inability to discover a concrete representation in which all of the axioms are satisfied does not indicate that the set of axioms under consideration is inconsistent. It may only indicate lack of ability or good fortune on the part of the investigator. However, if such a representation is found, it follows that the set is consistent.

These ideas may be understood better if an actual set of axioms be tested for consistency. A very simple set of axioms is the set employed in setting up simple order. The axioms are as follows:

(1) If a and b are not the same elements of C, then either a is less than b or b is less than a.

(2) If a is less than b, then a and b are not the same elements of C.

(3) If a is less than b, and b is less than c, then a is less than c.

In this set of axioms there appear several undefined terms. They are the letters, a, b, c, and C, and the expression, "is less than." Of course, the expression, "are not the same," may appear to have the same property, but it merely indicates lack of identity. The notion of identity belongs to the logicians, and mathematicians carefully avoid intrusion upon their domain. Mathematicians are supposed to have some intuitive notion of such concepts as the result of their contact, or lack of contact, with the logicians. For the necessary concrete representation of this system let a long single file of people be the representation of *C*. The small letters may be used to denote individual members of the file. The expression, "is less than," may be interpreted as "is standing somewhere in front of." It will then be seen at once that such a representation satisfies all of the axioms. As stated previously, this fact demonstrates the consistency of the set.

The notion of independence as applied to a set of axioms is somewhat simpler than the concept of consistency. A set of axioms is said to be independent if no one of them is logically deducible from the others. Sometimes the property of independence is thought of as being an aesthetic property, for a mathematician is much more pleased with a set of axioms if he knows that the number of them has been reduced to an absolute minimum. This would not be true as long as one of the axioms might be proved as the logical consequence of the others and could thus be classified as a theorem instead of an axiom. However, it must be distinctly understood that independence is not an absolutely necessary attribute of a set of axioms.

A satisfactory check for independence involves again the finding of a material or ideal representation for the axioms. However, this time it is desired to find a representation for which all of the axioms are satisfied except one. If such a representation can be found it serves to demonstrate that the one axiom can not be obtained as a consequence of the others. Again an illustration may serve to make this argument somewhat clearer. If in the set of axioms given previously for simple order, *C* is interpreted as the collection of all human beings from the start of time, the small letters are used to denote individual people, and the expression, "is less than," is interpreted to mean "is an ancestor of," then it will be readily observed that axioms (2) and (3) are true of the representation but axiom (1) is not. Consequently axiom (1) cannot be deduced from the other two, for if it could, it would likewise hold true for all situations for which the last two axioms are satisfied and one case has just been observed when this is not true. With a little thought, representations can be decided upon which will demonstrate the independence of the other two axioms. Of course, in more complicated sets of axioms the difficulty of applying the principle just considered is very great. Usually the investigator is forced to an ideal representation instead of a material one and this is very unfortunate. In any ideal picture the "intuitive" plays a very important role. Of course, as indicated previously, the intuitive may play a much more important role in the so-called material picture than some are willing to admit.

The generally accepted definition of categoricalness is based upon the very interesting concept of *isomorphism*. It is necessary, therefore, that isomorphism should be discussed first. Any collection of things which satisfies a given set of axioms after the proper particularization of the undefined terms is known as a universe. Suppose, then, that two universes exist which satisfy the same set of axioms. Suppose, moreover, that there exists a correspondence between the individual members of the two universes of such a nature that any statement which is true of the first universe is likewise true of the second when the individual members involved in the statement are replaced by the corresponding members of the second universe. As a further supposition let the converse of this latter statement be true. Then the two universes are said to be isomorphic with respect to the set of axioms. Of course, there may be a very large number of universes isomorphic with respect to the same set of axioms. These universes, in a sense, may be seen to be essentially the same universe, although the language used in discussing them may be superficially different.

It may be said, now, that a set of axioms is categorical when every two universes which satisfy it are isomorphic. The test for categoricalness will not be discussed here in any detail. Suffice it to say that the problem involves, of course, the establishment of the isomorphism of any two universes which satisfy the axioms. This is accomplished through the medium of a material representation which satisfies the axioms and which is then used in the sense of an intermediary to establish the isomorphism of any other two universes. Of course, if the universes were considered by pairs, the task becomes hopeless. Hence, the common procedure involves the consideration of general universes.

The Role of Logic

The second component involved in the making of a mathematical system is logic. It is not the intention here to give a detailed description of the principles of that ancient field of study. However, there are some aspects of logic so closely tied up with mathematical considerations that they must be mentioned in even such a brief work as this.

It was the sixth century B.C. when Pythagoras saw the "human necessity for a clear conception of proof on which all sane mortals could agree." It was Aristotle, however, who first pronounced certain laws which he conceived as the background of rigorous thought. His laws, as usually stated at the present time, are:

(1) A is A. (The law of identity.)
(2) Everything is either A or not-A. (The law of excluded middle.)
(3) Nothing is both A and not-A. (The law of contradiction.)

The last two of the above laws may be somewhat difficult of comprehension. By means of an interpretative device, used by most mathematicians and by many logicians, they become comparatively easy. Instead of thinking in terms of an abstract concept such as a property which several individual objects might possess, it is common for the mathematician to think in terms of the class of individuals which possess the property. For instance, if one should speak of the color, red, to a mathematician, he would probably not think of the abstraction which is denoted by red, rather he would think of the class of those objects which are red. This is approximately what is meant when it is said that the mathematician thinks of logical relations in extension rather than in intension. Moreover, the mathematician, as the logician, considers arbitrarily the product of two classes to be the new class composed of those members which are common to the two classes. Also the sum of two classes is taken as the new class composed of those members which belong to one or the other or both of the two given classes. So, then, if the minus sign be used to denote negation, the symbol 1 be used to denote the class of all objects (everything), and the symbol 0 be used to indicate the null class (nothing), the last two laws of Aristotelian logic become:

(2) $a + - a = 1.$ (The law of excluded middle.)
(3) $a \times - a = 0.$ (The law of contradiction.)

Traditional logic is concerned almost exclusively with relations between terms. The problem is the drawing of a conclusion as to what must be true or cannot be true of such relations. The laws just given along with the rules of syllogism are the available means for forming a decision.

Beyond this simple statement it must be realized that a vast system of logic has grown up, based upon laws which have to do with certain ideas which are taken as fundamental. Such words or concepts as class, all, negation, "either-or," etc., are jealously guarded by the logician as his own property. The basic laws, involving these ideas, are universals in the sense that they do not belong in their application to any one science or subject.

A new appreciation of the fact that the primitive words of logic are undefined words and that the so-called fundamental laws of logic are axioms in the mathematical sense has been observed with interest by mathematicians. In fact, the structure known as logic, built upon an axiomatic foundation, certainly resembles any mathematical structure. Boolean Algebra is becoming increasingly popular and such a system of logic built with the use of a symbolic language and erected upon an axiomatic basis is readily grasped by any mathematician. Incidentally, it may be remarked for the benefit of the uninitiated that Boolean Algebra is definitely Aristotelian in character and the last two laws of Aristotelian logic as stated in symbolic form are typical conclusions.

If, then, the so-called laws, which form the basis for traditional logic, are mere axioms, it is not surprising that there is a tendency to modify them or perhaps replace them altogether under various circumstances. Perhaps the time is rapidly approaching when the type of logic employed will be determined by the nature of the problem to be studied, just as the mathematician now debates what kind of mathematics is adapted to the problem under consideration. Korzybski has been disturbed about the law of identity and he apparently feels that its universal use is unwarranted. Brouwer has, likewise, challenged the universal use of the law of the excluded middle. Certainly it must be admitted that traditional logic is founded upon a philosophy of a determinate universe and it is very doubtful whether that kind of a doctrine is everywhere applicable. There certainly are questions which can not be answered by an unrestricted "yes" or an unrestricted "no." Many of such questions are beyond human capability to answer. Should one say, "But even in such questions there

is a proper answer"? Or should a place be reserved for indeterminacy in the universe and a logic be developed com-
patible with such a thought?

The real stimulus to the study of the actual nature of logic
as well as the possibility of having other kinds of logic in
addition to the traditional system of Aristotle was furnished
by the monumental work, "Principia Mathematica," by
Whitehead and Russell. The calculus of propositions developed in "Principia Mathematica" is definitely non-Aristotelian.
The technical interpretations of implication and identity as
employed in this work differ radically from the customary
meanings assigned to them. Nevertheless, deductions are
arrived at just as readily as through the use of traditional
methods which have no application in the "Principia."

It is possible to develop the system of logic employed in
the "Principia" by the use of a matrix method. For one who
is accustomed to the use of tables the device will be simple
to apply. If the truth or falsity of each of two propositions
is known, the nature of a particular relationship between the
two propositions may be determined by referring to a table
which is termed the matrix. The nature of other relationships may then be determined by virtue of their connection
to the relationship which is chosen as fundamental. By an
extension of this scheme of action Lukasiewicz has constructed systems of logic in which propositions do not necessarily have one or the other of the two truth possibilities,
"true" and "not-true," but can have any number of possibilities. Tarski has contributed to the further development of
these systems.

Such developments have caused C. I. Lewis to issue the
following declaration:

(1) There are no "laws of logic" which can be attributed
to the universe or to human reason in the traditional
fashion. What are ordinarily called "laws of logic" are
nothing but explicative or analytic statements of the meaning of certain concepts, such as truth and falsity, negation,
"either-or," implication, consistency, etc., which are taken
as basic.

A "system of logic" is nothing more than a convenient
collection of such concepts, together with the principles to
which they give rise by analysis of their meaning.

(2) There are an unlimited number of possible systems of logic, each such that every one of its laws is true and is applicable to deduction. These systems are alternatives in the sense that concepts and principles belonging to one cannot generally be introduced into another—because of fundamental differences of category.[5]

The significance of these results to mathematics is very great. Whereas it has been appreciated for some decades that the axiomatic component of mathematics is a variable one, now the task of the mathematician is considerably heightened by the realization that the logical component is also variable. No longer can the mathematician regard his logic as fixed and predetermined; rather he is faced by the fact that his very conclusions are relative to the type of logic employed as well as relative to the system of axioms involved.

Thus today the fields of mathematics and logic can not be considered separately. Nor are they so considered. Mathematicians are concerning themselves more and more with activities in logic. It was difficult for mathematicians to overcome the traditions of centuries and cultivate a critical attitude toward logic, but it was unavoidable.

Doubts and Uncertainties

The last word concerning the relation of mathematics and logic has not yet been said. One of the outstanding features of twentieth century mathematics has been the elaborate and critical examination of the very foundations of the subject. At the moment, doubts and uncertainties assail the mathematicians. Many students would not agree with the general point of view presented above, namely, that mathematics is the resultant of two components—a set of axioms and a system of logic. They would consider logic merely as a subdivision of a much vaster field called mathematics. On the other hand, there are those who contend that logic is an all-embracing subject, and mathematics is merely a minor aspect of the field.

As a matter of fact, there exist today three major schools of thought with regard to the "foundations of mathematics." These are usually designated as the *Formalist, the Logistic,* and the *Intuitionist* viewpoints.

The formalists acknowledge the leadership of the German

mathematician, David Hilbert. The viewpoint presented thus far in the present essay is basically that of the formalists, and it has been, until very recently, the view of most American mathematicians, who have been led in this country by such men as Oswald Veblen and E. V. Huntington. It is sometimes also referred to as the postulational school. The formalist thesis, briefly stated, is that pure mathematics is the science of the formal structure of symbols. For them, mathematics seeks to study the structure of objects by creating a system of symbols to represent them. Mathematics is thus concerned with the structural properties of symbolic systems, independent of their meaning. The individual symbols are devoid of meaning and have no significance except as they are related to other symbols. This does not mean that mathematics is an utterly meaningless game; on the contrary, the approach has proved exceedingly fruitful, particularly in geometry. However, the formalists have encountered disconcerting difficulties, chiefly in attempting to establish the validity of mathematics when approached from their point of view.

The logistic school, headed by Bertrand Russell and A. N. Whitehead, takes the position that pure mathematics is a branch of logic. Its forerunners were Peano and Frege. The culminating achievement of Russell and Whitehead was the monumental "Principia Mathematica," already alluded to above. This elaborate and massive work, exceedingly complex, and a masterpiece of logical beauty, attempts to reduce the whole of mathematics to logic. With amazing ingenuity they succeeded in defining elementary mathematical concepts (such as number, zero, operations of addition and multiplication, etc.) in terms of the accepted logical concepts (such as class, negation, "either-or," etc.). However, this approach has also run into difficulties, notably in connection with the modern theory of transfinite numbers, and so doubts have arisen in some quarters as to the success of their program.

The most recent school are the intuitionists, under the banner of the Dutch mathematician L. E. J. Brouwer, who was later joined by Hermann Weyl. Their thesis is that mathematics is founded on a basic intuition of the possibility of constructing an infinite series of numbers. Brouwer warns us that the symbolic structure usually identified with mathematics is merely the cloak of something much more fundamental in the way of a thought structure. He believes that when mathematicians manipulate the symbolic accompaniment of thought without due regard for the thought itself, trouble lies ahead. In short, the intuitionists do not look upon the body of mathematical truth as the objective structure which the formalist and logistic schools say that it is. For the intuitionists, mathematics can never be completely symbolized; mathematical thoughts are independent of the particular language used to express them. Knowledge of a given mathematical process must be such that the process clearly can be extended indefinitely. In other words, "existence" without the possibility of "construction" is inadmissible.

And so an atmosphere of confusion exists. As Max Black[6] has pointed out: "The logistic and formalist programmes have enormous difficulties to overcome if they are to be ultimately successful. For the logistic reduction of mathematics to logic breaks down at a crucial point, and a complete formalist proof of the consistency of mathematics is probably impossible. But the intuitionist doctrines require the larger part of mathematics to be rewritten, reject proofs that have long been accepted, abandon large portions of pure mathematics, and introduce a disheartening and almost impracticable complexity into those domains which are remodelled."

Still more recently, R. Carnap,[7] of Vienna and Chicago, has offered a program much broader than any of the above, which includes mathematics, logic, language, science, and metaphysics. Fundamentally it is an analysis of languages and their semantics. It is still too early to say to what it will lead.

What can be said of this state of affairs in which modern mathematics finds itself? We may be allowed to observe, first, that the fundamental concepts and methods of mathematics are in a perpetual state of evolution; secondly, that the effect of each point of view has been to modify profoundly the others; thirdly, that most mathematicians, by compromising, can work within one framework or another; and finally, that in the future there may be, not one mathematics, but many.

NOTES

[1] Bertrand Russell, *Principles of Mathematics*, Vol. 1, p. 1.

[2] "Mathematisches zu Aristoteles," in *Abhandlungen zur Gesch. d. math. Wissenschaften*, Heft 18, pp. 1–49.

[3] Bertrand Russell, "Philosophy of Logical Atomism," in *The Monist*, 1919.

[4] C. J. Keyser, *Mathematics and the Question of the Cosmic Mind*, p. 7.

[5] C. I. Lewis, "Alternative Systems of Logic," in *The Monist*, 1932, p. 483.

[6] Max Black, *The Nature of Mathematics*, 1934, p. 11.

[7] E. T. Bell, *The Development of Mathematics*, 1940, p. 529.

ON THE NATURE OF
MATHEMATICAL TRUTH

CARL G. HEMPEL

While we often speak glibly of "mathematical certainty," we may not be fully aware of the source of this certainty. The distinctive characteristic that differentiates mathematics from other forms of intellectual enterprise is the peculiar certainty and necessity of its results. This unique feature— the compulsion of its "truths"—is the very essence of mathematics.

In general, we may say that mathematical truth or certainty is relative truth: that is, a mathematical theorem is true relative to the postulates from which it is derived. If these postulates are true, the theorem is true; the theorem only reasserts more explicitly something implicitly stipulated in the postulates. This unique way of thinking is known as autonomous thinking. Mathematical truth is conditional truth; the conditions are self-imposed by the thinker. Postulate and theorem alike are devoid of empirical or factual content.

In the present essay, Professor Hempel develops this theme from the point of view of mathematics as a branch of logic. There are those who prefer to regard logic as a branch of mathematics. The past fifty years have witnessed a rapid and amazing development in the fields of symbolic logic and the logical foundations of mathematics. Dr. Hempel, primarily a philosopher, is an outstanding authority in his field.

On the Nature of Mathematical Truth*

The Problem

IT IS a basic principle of scientific inquiry that no proposition and no theory is to be accepted without adequate grounds. In empirical science, which includes both the natural and the social sciences, the grounds for the acceptance of a theory consist in the agreement of predictions based on the theory with empirical evidence obtained either by experiment or by systematic observation. But what are the grounds which sanction the acceptance of mathematics? That is the question I propose to discuss in the present paper. For reasons which will become clear subsequently, I shall use the term "mathematics" here to refer to arithmetic, algebra, and analysis—to the exclusion, in particular, of geometry.[1]

Are the Propositions of Mathematics Self-Evident Truths?

One of the several answers which have been given to our problem asserts that the truths of mathematics, in contradistinction to the hypotheses of empirical science, require neither factual evidence nor any other justification because they are "self-evident." This view, however, which ultimately relegates decisions as to mathematical truth to a feeling of self-evidence, encounters various difficulties. First of all, many mathematical theorems are so hard to establish that even to the specialist in the particular field they appear as anything but self-evident. Secondly, it is well known that some of the most interesting results of mathematics—especially in such fields as abstract set theory and topology—run counter to deeply ingrained intuitions and the customary kind of feeling of self-evidence. Thirdly, the existence of mathematical conjectures such as those of Goldbach and of Fermat, which are quite elementary in content and yet undecided up to this day, certainly shows that not all mathe-

* Reprinted from the *American Mathematical Monthly*, December, 1945, vol. 52, pp. 543–556. By permission of the author and the Mathematical Association of America.

matical truths can be self-evident. And finally, even if self-evidence were attributed only to the basic postulates of mathematics, from which all other mathematical propositions can be deduced, it would be pertinent to remark that judgments as to what may be considered as self-evident are subjective; they may vary from person to person and certainly cannot constitute an adequate basis for decisions as to the objective validity of mathematical propositions.

Is Mathematics the Most General Empirical Science?

According to another view, advocated especially by John Stuart Mill, mathematics is itself an empirical science which differs from the other branches such as astronomy, physics, chemistry, *etc.*, mainly in two respects: its subject matter is more general than that of any other field of scientific research, and its propositions have been tested and confirmed to a greater extent than those of even the most firmly established sections of astronomy or physics. Indeed, according to this view, the degree to which the laws of mathematics have been borne out by the past experiences of mankind is so overwhelming that—unjustifiably—we have come to think of mathematical theorems as qualitatively different from the well-confirmed hypotheses or theories of other branches of science: we consider them as certain, while other theories are thought of as at best "very probable" or very highly confirmed.

But this view, too, is open to serious objections. From a hypothesis which is empirical in character—such as, for example, Newton's law of gravitation—it is possible to derive predictions to the effect that under certain specified conditions certain specified observable phenomena will occur. The actual occurrence of these phenomena constitutes confirming evidence, their non-occurrence disconfirming evidence for the hypothesis. It follows in particular that an empirical hypothesis is theoretically disconfirmable; *i.e.*, it is possible to indicate what kind of evidence, if actually encountered, would disconfirm the hypothesis. In the light of this remark, consider now a simple "hypothesis" from arithmetic: $3 + 2 = 5$. If this is actually an empirical generalization of past experiences, then it must be possible to state what kind of evidence would oblige us to concede the hypothesis was not generally true after all. If any disconfirming evidence for the given proposition can be thought of, the following illustration might well be typical of it: We place some microbes on a slide, putting down first three of them and then another two. Afterwards we count all the microbes to test whether in this instance 3 and 2 actually added up to 5. Suppose now that we counted 6 microbes altogether. Would we consider this as an empirical disconfirmation of the given proposition, or at least as a proof that it does not apply to microbes? Clearly not; rather, we would assume we had made a mistake in counting or that one of the microbes had split in two between the first and the second count. But under no circumstances could the phenomenon just described invalidate the arithmetical proposition in question; for the latter asserts nothing whatever about the behavior of microbes; it merely states that any set consisting of $3 + 2$ objects may also be said to consist of 5 objects. And this is so because the symbols "$3 + 2$" and "5" denote the same number: they are synonymous by virtue of the fact that the symbols "2," "3," "5," and "$+$" are *defined* (or tacitly understood) in such a way that the above identity holds as a consequence of the meaning attached to the concepts involved in it.

The Analytic Character of Mathematical Propositions

The statement that $3 + 2 = 5$, then, is true for similar reasons as, say, the assertion that no sexagenarian is 45 years of age. Both are true simply by virtue of definitions or of similar stipulations which determine the meaning of the key terms involved. Statements of this kind share certain important characteristics: Their validation naturally requires no empirical evidence; they can be shown to be true by a mere analysis of the meaning attached to the terms which occur in them. In the language of logic, sentences of this kind are called analytic or true a priori, which is to indicate that their truth is logically independent of, or logically prior to, any experiential evidence.[2] And while the statements of empirical science, which are synthetic and can be validated only a posteriori, are constantly subject to revision in the light of new evidence, the truth of an analytic statement can be established definitely, once and for all. However, this characteristic "theoretical certainty" of analytic propositions has to be paid for at a high price: An analytic statement conveys no factual information. Our statement about sexagenarians, for example, asserts nothing that could possibly conflict with any factual evidence: it has no factual implications, no empirical content; and it is precisely for this reason that the statement can be validated without recourse to empirical evidence.

Let us illustrate this view of the nature of mathematical propositions by reference to another, frequently cited, example of a mathematical—or rather logical—truth, namely the proposition that whenever $a = b$ and $b = c$ then $a = c$. On what grounds can this so-called "transitivity of identity" be asserted? Is it of an empirical nature and hence at least theoretically disconfirmable by empirical evidence? Suppose, for example, that $a, b, c,$ are certain shades of green, and that as far as we can see, $a = b$ and $b = c$, but clearly $a \neq c$. This phenomenon actually occurs under certain conditions; do we consider it as disconfirming evidence for the proposition under consideration? Undoubtedly not; we would argue that if $a \neq c$, it is impossible that $a = b$ and also $b = c$; between the terms of at least one of these latter pairs, there must obtain a difference, though perhaps only a subliminal one. And we would dismiss the possibility of empirical disconfirmation, and indeed the idea that an empirical test should be relevant here, on the grounds that identity is a transitive relation by virtue of its definition or by virtue of the basic postulates governing it.[3] Hence, the principle in question is true a priori.

Mathematics as an Axiomatized Deductive System

I have argued so far that the validity of mathematics rests neither on its alleged self-evidential character nor on any empirical basis, but derives from the stipulations which determine the meaning of the mathematical concepts, and that the propositions of mathematics are therefore essentially "true by definition." This latter statement, however, is obviously oversimplified and needs restatement and a more careful justification.

For the rigorous development of a mathematical theory proceeds not simply from a set of definitions but rather from a set of non-definitional propositions which are not proved within the theory; these are the postulates or axioms of the theory.[4] They are formulated in terms of certain basic or primitive concepts for which no definitions are provided within the theory. It is sometimes asserted that the postulates themselves represent "implicit definitions" of the primitive terms. Such a characterization of the postulates, however, is misleading. For while the postulates do limit, in a specific sense, the meanings that can possibly be ascribed to the primitives, any self-consistent postulate system admits, nevertheless, many different interpretations of the primitive terms (this will soon be illustrated), whereas a set of definitions in the strict sense of the word determines the meanings of the definienda in a unique fashion.

Once the primitive terms and the postulates have been laid down, the entire theory is completely determined; it is derivable from its postulational basis in the following sense: Every term of the theory is definable in terms of the primitives, and every proposition of the theory is logically deducible from the postulates. To be entirely precise, it is necessary also to specify the principles of logic which are to be used in the proof of the propositions, *i.e.* in their deduction from the postulates. These principles can be stated quite explicitly. They fall into two groups: Primitive sentences, or postulates, of logic (such as: If p and q is the case, then p is the case), and rules of deduction or inference (including, for example, the familiar modus ponens rule and the rules of substitution which make it possible to infer, from a general proposition, any one of its substitution instances). A more detailed discussion of the structure and content of logic would, however, lead too far afield in the context of this article.

Peano's Axiom System as a Basis for Mathematics

Let us now consider a postulate system from which the entire arithmetic of the natural numbers can be derived. This system was devised by the Italian mathematician and logician G. Peano (1858–1932). The primitives of this system are the terms "0," "number," and "successor." While, of course, no definition of these terms is given within the theory, the symbol "0" is intended to designate the number 0 in its usual meaning, while the term "number" is meant to refer to the natural numbers 0, 1, 2, 3 . . . exclusively. By the successor of a natural number n, which will sometimes briefly be called n', is meant the natural number immediately following n in the natural order. Peano's system contains the following 5 postulates:

P1. 0 is a number
P2. The successor of any number is a number

P3. No two numbers have the same successor

P4. 0 is not the successor of any number

P5. If P is a property such that (a) 0 has the property P, and (b) whenever a number n has the property P, then the successor of n also has the property P, then every number has the property P.

The last postulate embodies the principle of mathematical induction and illustrates in a very obvious manner the enforcement of a mathematical "truth" by stipulation. The construction of elementary arithmetic on this basis begins with the definition of the various natural numbers. 1 is defined as the successor of 0, or briefly as $0'$; 2 as $1'$, 3 as $2'$, and so on. By virtue of P2, this process can be continued indefinitely; because of P3 (in combination with P5), it never leads back to one of the numbers previously defined, and in view of P4, it does not lead back to 0 either.

As the next step, we can set up a definition of addition which expresses in a precise form the idea that the addition of any natural number to some given number may be considered as a repeated addition of 1; the latter operation is readily expressible by means of the successor relation. This definition of addition runs as follows:

D1. (a) $n + 0 = n$;   (b) $n + k' = (n + k)'$.

The two stipulations of this recursive definition completely determine the sum of any two integers. Consider, for example, the sum $3 + 2$. According to the definitions of the numbers 2 and 1, we have $3 + 2 = 3 + 1' = 3 + (0')'$; by D1 (b), $3 + (0')' = (3 + 0')' = ((3 + 0)')'$; but by D1 (a), and by the definitions of the numbers 4 and 5, $((3 + 0)')' = (3')' = 4' = 5$. This proof also renders more explicit and precise the comments made earlier in this paper on the truth of the proposition that $3 + 2 = 5$: Within the Peano system of arithmetic, its truth flows not merely from the definition of the concepts involved, but also from the postulates that govern these various concepts. (In our specific example, the postulates P1 and P2 are presupposed to guarantee that 1, 2, 3, 4, 5 are numbers in Peano's system; the general proof that D1 determines the sum of any two numbers also makes use of P5). If we call the postulates and definitions of an axiomatized theory the "stipulations" concerning the concepts of that theory, then we may say now that the propositions of the arithmetic of the natural numbers are true by virtue of the stipulations which have been laid down initially for the arithmetical concepts. (Note, incidentally, that our proof of the formula "3 + 2 = 5" repeatedly made use of the transitivity of identity; the latter is accepted here as one of the rules of logic which may be used in the proof of any arithmetical theorem; it is, therefore, included among Peano's postulates no more than any other principle of logic.)

Now, the multiplication of natural numbers may be defined by means of the following recursive definition, which expresses in a rigorous form the idea that a product nk of two integers may be considered as the sum of k terms each of which equals n.

D2. (a) $n \cdot 0 = 0$;   (b) $n \cdot k' = n \cdot k + n$.

It now is possible to prove the familiar general laws governing addition and multiplication, such as the commutative, associative, and distributive laws $(n + k = k + n,$ $n \cdot k = k \cdot n;\ n + (k + l) = (n + k) + l,\ n \cdot (k \cdot l) = (n \cdot k) \cdot l;\ n \cdot (k + l) = (n \cdot k) + (n \cdot l))$. In terms of addition and multiplication, the inverse operations of subtraction and division can then be defined. But it turns out that these "cannot always be performed"; *i.e.*, in contradistinction to the sum and the product, the difference and the quotient are not defined for every couple of numbers; for example, $7 - 10$ and $7 \div 10$ are undefined. This situation suggests an enlargement of the number system by the introduction of negative and of rational numbers.

It is sometimes held that in order to effect this enlargement, we have to "assume" or else to "postulate" the existence of the desired additional kinds of numbers with properties that make them fit to fill the gaps of subtraction and division. This method of simply postulating what we want has its advantages; but, as Bertrand Russell[5] puts it, they are the same as the advantages of theft over honest toil; and it is a remarkable fact that the negative as well as the rational numbers can be obtained from Peano's primitives by the honest toil of constructing explicit definitions for them, without the introduction of any new postulates or assumptions whatsoever. Every positive and negative integer—in contradistinction to a natural number which has no sign—is definable as a certain set of ordered couples of natural numbers; thus, the integer $+ 2$ is definable as the set of all ordered couples (m, n) of natural numbers where $m = n + 2$; the integer $- 2$ is the set of all ordered couples (m, n) of natural numbers with $n = m + 2$. Similarly, rational numbers are defined as classes of ordered couples of integers. The various arithmetical operations can then be defined with reference to these new types of numbers, and the validity of all the arithmetical laws governing these operations can be proved by virtue of nothing more than Peano's postulates and the definitions of the various arithmetical concepts involved.

The much broader system thus obtained is still incomplete in the sense that not every number in it has a square root, and more generally, not every algebraic equation whose coefficients are all numbers of the system has a solution in the system. This suggests further expansions of the number system by the introduction of real and finally of complex numbers. Again, this enormous extension can be effected by mere definition, without the introduction of a single new postulate.[6] On the basis thus obtained, the various arithmetical and algebraic operations can be defined for the numbers of the new system, the concepts of function, of limit, of derivative and integral can be introduced, and the familiar theorems pertaining to these concepts can be proved, so that finally the huge system of mathematics as here delimited rests on the narrow basis of Peano's system: Every concept of mathematics can be defined by means of Peano's three primitives, and every proposition of mathematics can be deduced from the five postulates enriched by the definitions of the non-primitive terms.[7] These deductions can be carried out, in most cases, by means of nothing more than the principles of formal logic; the proof of some theorems concerning real numbers, however, requires one assumption which is not usually included among the latter. This is the so-called axiom of choice. It asserts that given a class of mutually exclusive classes, none of which is empty, there exists at least one class which has exactly one element in common with each of the given classes. By virtue of this principle and the rules of formal logic, the content of all of mathematics can thus be derived from Peano's modest system—a remarkable achievement in systematizing the content of mathematics and clarifying the foundations of its validity.

Interpretations of Peano's Primitives

As a consequence of this result, the whole system of mathematics might be said to be true by virtue of mere definitions (namely, of the non-primitive mathematical terms) provided that the five Peano postulates are true. However, strictly speaking, we cannot, at this juncture, refer to the Peano postulates as propositions which are either true or false, for they contain three primitive terms which have not been assigned any specific meaning. All we can assert so far is that any specific interpretation of the primitives which satisfies the five postulates—*i.e.*, turns them into true statements—will also satisfy all the theorems deduced from them. But for Peano's system, there are several—indeed, infinitely many—interpretations which will do this. For example, let us understand by 0 the origin of a half-line, by the successor of a point on that half-line the point 1 cm. behind it, counting from the origin, and by a number any point which is either the origin or can be reached from it by a finite succession of steps each of which leads from one point to its successor. It can then readily be seen that all the Peano postulates as well as the ensuing theorems turn into true propositions, although the interpretation given to the primitives is certainly not the customary one, which was mentioned earlier. More generally, it can be shown that every progression of elements of any kind provides a true interpretation, or a "model," of the Peano system. This example illustrates our earlier observation that a postulate system cannot be regarded as a set of "implicit definitions" for the primitive terms: The Peano system permits of many different interpretations, whereas in everyday as well as in scientific language, we attach one specific meaning to the concepts of arithmetic. Thus, *e.g.*, in scientific and in everyday discourse, the concept 2 is understood in such a way that from the statement "Mr. Brown as well as Mr. Cope, but no one else is in the office, and Mr. Brown is not the same person as Mr. Cope," the conclusion "Exactly two persons are in the office" may be validly inferred. But the stipulations laid down in Peano's system for the natural numbers, and for the number 2 in particular, do not enable us to draw this conclusion; they do not "implicitly determine" the customary meaning of the concept 2 or of the other arithmetical concepts. And the mathematician cannot acquiesce at this deficiency by arguing that he is not concerned with the customary meaning of the mathematical concepts; for in proving, say, that every positive real number has exactly two real square roots, he is himself using the concept 2 in its customary meaning, and his very theorem cannot be proved unless we presuppose more about the number 2 than is stipulated in the Peano system.

If therefore mathematics is to be a correct theory of the mathematical concepts in their intended meaning, it is not sufficient for its validation to have shown that the entire system is derivable from the Peano postulates plus suitable definitions; rather, we have to inquire further whether the Peano postulates are actually true when the primitives are understood in their customary meaning. This question, of course, can be answered only after the customary meaning of the terms "0," "natural number," and "successor" has been clearly defined. To this task we now turn.

Definition of the Customary Meaning of the Concepts of Arithmetic in Purely Logical Terms

At first blush, it might seem a hopeless undertaking to try to define these basic arithmetical concepts without presupposing other terms of arithmetic, which would involve us in a circular procedure. However, quite rigorous definitions of the desired kind can indeed be formulated, and it can be shown that for the concepts so defined, all Peano postulates turn into true statements. This important result is due to the research of the German logician G. Frege (1848–1925) and to the subsequent systematic and detailed work of the contemporary English logicians and philosophers B. Russell and A. N. Whitehead. Let us consider briefly the basic ideas underlying these definitions.[8]

A natural number—or, in Peano's term, a number—in its customary meaning can be considered as a characteristic of certain *classes* of objects. Thus, *e.g.*, the class of the apostles has the number 12, the class of the Dionne quintuplets the number 5, any couple the number 2, and so on. Let us now express precisely the meaning of the assertion that a certain class C has the number 2, or briefly, that $n(C) = 2$. Brief reflection will show that the following definiens is adequate in the sense of the customary meaning of the concept 2: There is some object x and some object y such that (1) $x \epsilon C$ (*i.e.*, x is an element of C) and $y \epsilon C$, (2) $x \neq y$, and (3) if z is any object such that $z \epsilon C$, then either $z = x$ or z

$= y$. (Note that on the basis of this definition it becomes indeed possible to infer the statement "The number of persons in the office is 2" from "Mr. Brown as well as Mr. Cope, but no one else is in the office, and Mr. Brown is not identical with Mr. Cope"; C is here the class of persons in the office.) Analogously, the meaning of the statement that $n(C) = 1$ can be defined thus: There is some x with that $x \epsilon C$, and any object y such that $y \epsilon C$ is identical with x. Similarly, the customary meaning of the statement that $n(C) = 0$ is this: There is no object such that $x \epsilon C$.

The general pattern of these definitions clearly lends itself to the definition of any natural number. Let us note especially that in the definitions thus obtained, the definiens never contains any arithmetical term, but merely expressions taken from the field of formal logic, including the signs of identity and difference. So far, we have defined only the meaning of such phrases as "$n(C) = 2$," but we have given no definition for the numbers 0, 1, 2, $\cdots$ apart from this context. This desideratum can be met on the basis of the consideration that 2 is that property which is common to all couples, *i.e.*, to all classes C such that $n(C) = 2$. This common property may be conceptually represented by the class of all those classes which share this property. Thus we arrive at the definition: 2 is the class of all couples, *i.e.*, the class of all classes C for which $n(C) = 2$. This definition is by no means circular because the concept of couple—in other words, the meaning of "$n(C) = 2$"—has been previously defined without any reference to the number 2. Analogously, 1 is the class of all unit classes, *i.e.*, the class of all classes C for which $n(C) = 1$. Finally, 0 is the class of all null classes, *i.e.*, the class of all classes without elements. And as there is only one such class, 0 is simply the class whose only element is the null class. Clearly, the customary meaning of any given natural number can be defined in this fashion.[9] In order to characterize the intended interpretation of Peano's primitives, we actually need, of all the definitions here referred to, only that of the number 0. It remains to define the terms "successor" and "integer."

The definition of "successor," whose precise formulation involves too many niceties to be stated here, is a careful expression of a simple idea which is illustrated by the following example: Consider the number 5, *i.e.*, the class of all quintuplets. Let us select an arbitrary one of these quintuplets and add to it an object which is not yet one of its members. 5′, the successor of 5, may then be defined as the number applying to the set thus obtained (which, of course, is a sextuplet). Finally, it is possible to formulate a definition of the customary meaning of the concept of natural number; this definition, which again cannot be given here, expresses, in a rigorous form, the idea that the class of the natural numbers consists of the number 0, its successor, the successor of that successor, and so on.

If the definitions here characterized are carefully written out—this is one of the cases where the techniques of symbolic, or mathematical, logic prove indispensable—it is seen that the definiens of every one of them contains exclusively terms from the field of pure logic. In fact, it is possible to state the customary interpretation of Peano's primitives, and thus also the meaning of every concept definable by means of them—and that includes every concept of mathematics— in terms of the following 7 expressions, in addition to variables such as "*x*" and "*C*": *not, and, if—then; for every object* x *it is the case that* . . . ; *there is some object* x *such that* . . . ; x *is an* element *of class* C; *the class of all things* x *such that.* . . . And it is even possible to reduce the number of logical concepts needed to a mere four: The first three of the concepts just mentioned are all definable in terms of *"neither—nor,"* and the fifth is definable by means of the fourth and *"neither—nor."* Thus, all the concepts of mathematics prove definable in terms of four concepts of pure logic. (The definition of one of the more complex concepts of mathematics in terms of the four primitives just mentioned may well fill hundreds or even thousands of pages; but clearly this affects in no way the theoretical importance of the result just obtained; it does, however, show the great convenience and indeed practical indispensability for mathematics of having a large system of highly complex defined concepts available.)

The Truth of Peano's Postulates in Their Customary Interpretation

The definitions characterized in the preceding section may be said to render precise and explicit the customary meaning of the concepts of arithmetic. Moreover—and this is crucial for the question of the validity of mathematics—it can be shown that the Peano postulates all turn into true propositions if the primitives are construed in accordance with the definitions just considered.

Thus, P1 (0 is a number) is true because the class of all numbers—*i.e.,* natural numbers—was defined as consisting of 0 and all its successors. The truth of P2 (The successor of any number is a number) follows from the same definition. This is true also of P5, the principle of mathematical induction. To prove this, however, we would have to resort to the precise definition of "integer" rather than the loose description given of that definition above. P4 (0 is not the successor of any number) is seen to be true as follows: By virtue of the definition of "successor," a number which is a successor of some number can apply only to classes which contain at least one element; but the number 0, by definition, applies to a class if and only if that class is empty. While the truth of P1, P2, P4, P5 can be inferred from the above definitions simply by means of the principles of logic, the proof of P3 (No two numbers have the same successor) presents a certain difficulty. As was mentioned in the preceding section, the definition of the successor of a number n is based on the process of adding, to a class of n elements, one element not yet contained in that class. Now if there should exist only a finite number of things altogether then this process could not be continued indefinitely, and P3 which (in conjunction with P1 and P2) implies that the integers form an infinite set, would be false. This difficulty can be met by the introduction of a special "axiom of infinity,"[10] which asserts, in effect, the existence of infinitely many objects, and thus makes P3 demonstrable. The axiom of infinity does not belong to the generally recognized laws of logic; but it is capable of expression in purely logical terms and may be considered as an additional postulate of modern logical theory.

Mathematics as a Branch of Logic

As was pointed out earlier, all the theorems of arithmetic, algebra, and analysis can be deduced from the Peano postulates and the definitions of those mathematical terms which are not primitives in Peano's system. This deduction requires only the principles of logic plus, in certain cases, the axiom of choice. By combining this result with what has just been said about the Peano system, the following conclusion is obtained, which is also known as *the thesis of logicism concerning the nature of mathematics*:

Mathematics is a branch of logic. It can be derived from logic in the following sense:

a. All the concepts of mathematics, *i.e.* of arithmetic, algebra, and analysis, can be defined in terms of four concepts of pure logic.

b. All the theorems of mathematics can be deduced from those definitions by means of the principles of logic (including the axioms of infinity and of choice).[11]

In this sense it can be said that the propositions of the system of mathematics as here delimited are true by virtue of the definitions of the mathematical concepts involved, or that they make explicit certain characteristics with which we have endowed our mathematical concepts by definition. The propositions of mathematics have, therefore, the same unquestionable certainty which is typical of such propositions as "All bachelors are unmarried," but they also share the complete lack of empirical content which is associated with that certainty: the propositions of mathematics are devoid of all factual content; they convey no information whatever on any empirical subject matter.

On the Applicability of Mathematics to Empirical Subject Matter

This result seems to be irreconcilable with the fact that after all mathematics has proved to be eminently applicable to empirical subject matter, and that indeed the greater part of present-day scientific knowledge has been reached only through continual reliance on and application of the propositions of mathematics. Let us try to clarify this apparent paradox by reference to some examples.

Suppose that we are examining a certain amount of some gas, whose volume v, at a certain fixed temperature, is found to be 9 cubic feet when the pressure p is 4 atmospheres. And let us assume further that the volume of the gas for the same temperature and $p = 6$ *at.*, is predicted by means of Boyle's law. Using elementary arithmetic we reason thus: For corresponding values of v and p, $vp = c$, and $v = 9$ when $p = 4$; hence $c = 36$: Therefore, when $p = 6$, then $v = 6$. Suppose that this prediction is borne out by subsequent test. Does that show that the arithmetic used has a predictive power of its own, that its propositions have factual implications? Certainly not. All the predictive power here deployed, all the empirical content exhibited stems from the initial data and from Boyle's law, which asserts that $vp = c$ for *any* two corresponding values of v and p, hence also for $v = 9$, $p = 4$, and for $p = 6$ and the corresponding value of v.[12] The function of the mathematics here applied is not predictive at all; rather, it is analytic or explicative: it renders explicit certain assumptions or assertions which are included in the content of the premises of the argument (in our case, these consist of Boyle's law plus the additional data); mathematical reasoning reveals that those premises contain—hidden in them, as it were—an assertion about the case as yet unobserved. In accepting our premises—so arithmetic reveals—we have—knowingly or unknowingly—already accepted the implication that the p value in question is 6. Mathematical as well as logical reasoning is a conceptual technique of making explicit what is implicitly contained in a set of premises. The conclusions to which this technique leads assert nothing that is *theoretically new* in the sense of not being contained in the content of the premises. But the results obtained may well be *psychologically new*: we may not have been aware, before using the techniques of logic and mathematics, what we committed ourselves to in accepting a certain set of assumptions or assertions.

A similar analysis is possible in all other cases of applied mathematics, including those involving, say, the calculus. Consider, for example, the hypothesis that a certain object, moving in a specified electric field, will undergo a constant acceleration of 5 feet/sec². For the purpose of testing this hypothesis, we might derive from it, by means of two successive integrations, the prediction that if the object is at rest at the beginning of the motion, then the distance covered by it at any time t is $\frac{5}{2}t^2$ feet. This conclusion may clearly be psychologically new to a person not acquainted with the subject, but it is not theoretically new; the content of the conclusion is already contained in that of the hypothesis about the constant acceleration. And indeed, here as well as in the case of the compression of a gas, a failure of the prediction to come true would be considered as indicative of the factual incorrectness of at least one of the premises involved (*e.g.*, of Boyle's law in its application to the particular gas), but never as a sign that the logical and mathematical principles involved might be unsound.

Thus, in the establishment of empirical knowledge, mathematics (as well as logic) has, so to speak, the function of a theoretical juice extractor: the techniques of mathematical and logical theory can produce no more juice of factual information than is contained in the assumptions to which they are applied; but they may produce a great deal more juice of this kind than might have been anticipated upon a first intuitive inspection of those assumptions which form the raw material for the extractor.

At this point, it may be well to consider briefly the status of those mathematical disciplines which are not outgrowths of arithmetic and thus of logic; these include in particular topology, geometry, and the various branches of abstract algebra, such as the theory of groups, lattices, fields, *etc.* Each of these disciplines can be developed as a purely deductive system on the basis of a suitable set of postulates. If P be the conjunction of the postulates for a given theory, then the proof of a proposition T of that theory consists in deducing T from P by means of the principles of formal logic. What is established by the proof is therefore not the truth of T, but rather the fact that T is true provided that the postulates are. But since both P and T contain certain primitive terms of the theory, to which no specific meaning is assigned, it is not strictly possible to speak of the truth of either P or T; it is therefore more adequate to state the point as follows: If a proposition T is logically deduced from P, then every specific interpretation of the primitives which turns all the postulates of P into true statements, will also render T a true statement. Up to this point, the analysis is exactly analogous to that of arithmetic as based on Peano's set of postulates. In the case of arithmetic, however, it proved possible to go a step further, namely to define the customary meanings of the primitives in terms of purely logical concepts and to show that the postulates—and therefore also the theorems—of arithmetic are unconditionally true by virtue of these definitions. An analogous procedure is not applicable to those disciplines which are not outgrowths of arithmetic: The primitives of the various branches of abstract algebra have no specific "customary meaning"; and if geometry in its customary interpretation is thought of as a theory of the structure of physical space, then its primitives have to be construed as referring to certain types of physical entities, and the question of the truth of a geometrical theory in this interpretation turns into an *empirical* problem.[13] For the purpose of applying any one of these non-arithmetical disciplines to some specific field of mathematics or empirical science, it is therefore necessary first to assign to the primitives some specific meaning and then to ascertain whether in this interpretation the postulates turn into true statements. If this is the case, then we can be sure that all the theorems are true statements too, because they are logically derived from the postulates and thus simply explicate the content of the latter in the given interpretation. In their application to empirical subject matter, therefore, these mathematical theories no less than those which grow out of arithmetic and ultimately out of pure logic, have the function of an analytic tool, which brings to light the implications of a given set of assumptions but adds nothing to their content.

But while mathematics in no case contributes anything to the content of our knowledge of empirical matters, it is entirely indispensable as an instrument for the validation and even for the linguistic expression of such knowledge: The majority of the more far-reaching theories in empirical science —including those which lend themselves most eminently to prediction or to practical application are stated with the help of mathematical concepts; the formulation of these theories makes use, in particular, of the number system, and of functional relationships among different metrical variables. Furthermore, the scientific test of these theories, the establishment of predictions by means of them, and finally their practical application, all require the deduction, from the general theory, of certain specific consequences; and such deduction would be entirely impossible without the techniques of mathematics which reveal what the given general theory implicitly asserts about a certain special case.

Thus, the analysis outlined on these pages exhibits the system of mathematics as a vast and ingenious conceptual structure without empirical content and yet an indispensable and powerful theoretical instrument for the scientific understanding and mastery of the world of our experience.

NOTES

[1] A discussion of the status of geometry is given in my article, "Geometry and Empirical Science," *American Mathematical Monthly*, vol. 52, pp. 7–17, 1945.

[2] The objection is sometimes raised that without certain types of experience, such as encountering several objects of the same kind, the integers and the arithmetical operations with them would never have been invented, and that therefore the propositions of

arithmetic do have an empirical basis. This type of argument, however, involves a confusion of the logical and the psychological meaning of the term "basis." It may very well be the case that certain experiences occasion psychologically the formation of arithmetical ideas and in this sense form an empirical "basis" for them; but this point is entirely irrelevant for the logical questions as to the *grounds* on which the propositions of arithmetic may be accepted as true. The point made above is that no empirical "basis" or evidence whatever is needed to establish the truth of the propositions of arithmetic.

[3] A precise account of the definition and the essential characteristics of the identity relation may be found in A. Tarski, *Introduction to Logic*, New York, 1941, Ch. III.

[4] For a lucid and concise account of the axiomatic method, see A. Tarski, *l.c.*, Ch. VI.

[5] Bertrand Russell, *Introduction to Mathematical Philosophy*, New York and London, 1919, p. 71.

[6] For a more detailed account of the construction of the number system on Peano's basis, *cf.* Bertrand Russell, *l.c.*, esp. Chs. I and VII. A rigorous and concise presentation of that construction, beginning, however, with the set of all integers rather than that of the natural numbers, may be found in G. Birkhoff and S. MacLane, *A Survey of Modern Algebra*, New York, 1941, Chs. I, II, III, V. For a general survey of the construction of the number system, *cf.* also J. W. Young, *Lectures on the Fundamental Concepts of Algebra and Geometry*, New York, 1911, esp. lectures X, XI, XII.

[7] As a result of very deep-reaching investigations carried out by K. Gödel it is known that arithmetic, and *a fortiori* mathematics, is an incomplete theory in the following sense: While all those propositions which belong to the classical systems of arithmetic, algebra, and analysis can indeed be derived, in the sense characterized above, from the Peano postulates, there exist nevertheless other propositions which can be expressed in purely arithmetical terms, and which are true, but which cannot be derived from the Peano system. And more generally: For any postulate system of arithmetic (or of mathematics for that matter) which is not self-contradictory, there exist propositions which are true, and which can be stated in purely arithmetical terms, but which cannot be derived from that postulate system. In other words, it is impossible to construct a postulate system which is not self-contradictory, and which contains among its consequences all true propositions which can be formulated within the language of arithmetic.

This fact does not, however, affect the result outlined above, namely, that it is possible to deduce, from the Peano postulates and the additional definitions of non-primitive terms, all those propositions which constitute the classical theory of arithmetic, algebra, and analysis; and it is to these propositions that I refer above and subsequently as the propositions of mathematics.

[8] For a more detailed discussion, *cf*. Russell, *l.c.*, II, III, IV. A complete technical development of the idea can be found in the great standard work in mathematical logic, A. N. Whitehead and B. Russell, *Principia Mathematica,* Cambridge, England, 1910–1913. For a very precise recent development of the theory, see W. V. O. Quine, *Mathematical Logic,* New York 1940. A specific discussion of the Peano system and its interpretations from the viewpoint of semantics is included in R. Carnap, "Foundations of Logic and Mathematics," *International Encyclopedia of Unified Science,* vol. I, no. 3, Chicago, 1939; especially sections 14, 17, 18.

[9] The assertion that the definitions given above state the "customary" meaning of the arithmetical terms involved is to be understood in the logical, not the psychological sense of the term "meaning." It would obviously be absurd to claim that the above definitions express "what everybody has in mind" when talking about numbers and the various operations that can be performed with them. What is achieved by those definitions is rather a "logical reconstruction" of the concepts of arithmetic in the sense that if the definitions are accepted, then those statements in science and everyday discourse which involve arithmetical terms can be interpreted coherently and systematically in such a manner that they are capable of objective validation. The statement about the two persons in the office provides a very elementary illustration of what is meant here.

[10] *Cf*. Bertrand Russell, *l.c.*, p. 24 and Ch. XIII.

[11] The principles of logic developed in modern systems of formal logic embody certain restrictions as compared with those logical rules which had been rather generally accepted as sound until about the turn of the twentieth century. At that time, the discovery of the famous paradoxes of logic, especially of Russell's paradox (*cf*. Russell, *l.c.*, Ch. XIII), revealed the fact that the logical principles implicit in customary mathematical reasoning involved contradictions and therefore had to be curtailed in one manner or another.

[12] Note that we may say "hence" by virtue of the rule of substitution, which is one of the rules of logical inference.

[13] For a more detailed discussion of this point, *cf*. the article mentioned in reference 1.

GEOMETRY AND EMPIRICAL SCIENCE

Carl G. Hempel

In many respects, geometry typifies the development of all mathematics. The pattern is somewhat as follows. Initially, the human mind manifests perception, i.e., observation and manipulation of physical objects leads to crude generalizations. These in turn become refined, and eventually there crystallize highly idealized abstractions, devoid of all measurable and empirical attributes. To satisfy some deep, inner compulsion, intellectual man cannot rest until he has evolved from these generalized abstractions a satisfying pattern of some sort.

Thus early geometry grew out of the empirical experience of the ancient Egyptian "earth measurement," and was transformed by the Greeks into an idealized logical system, albeit crude by contemporary standards. During the seventeenth and eighteenth centuries it was elaborated by Desargues, Monge, Poncelet, Steiner and others. Toward the latter part of the nineteenth century geometry was made more universal by the contributions of Bolyai, Lobachevsky and Riemann, and at the turn of the century was made more rigorous by the work of Hilbert, Veblen, Peano, and a host of others.

Geometry and Empirical Science*

1. *Introduction*

THE MOST distinctive characteristic which differentiates mathematics from the various branches of empirical science, and which accounts for its fame as the queen of the sciences, is no doubt the peculiar certainty and necessity of its results. No proposition in even the most advanced parts of empirical science can ever attain this status; a hypothesis concerning "matters of empirical fact" can at best acquire what is loosely called a high probability or a high degree of confirmation on the basis of the relevant evidence available; but however well it may have been confirmed by careful tests, the possibility can never be precluded that it will have to be discarded later in the light of new and disconfirming evidence. Thus, all the theories and hypotheses of empirical science share this provisional character of being established and accepted "until further notice," whereas a mathematical theorem, once proved, is established once and for all; it holds with that particular certainty which no subsequent empirical discoveries, however unexpected and extraordinary, can ever affect to the slightest extent. It is the purpose of this paper to examine the nature of that proverbial "mathematical certainty" with special reference to geometry, in an attempt to shed some light on the question as to the validity of geometrical theories, and their significance for our knowledge of the structure of physical space.

The nature of mathematical truth can be understood through an analysis of the method by means of which it is established. On this point I can be very brief: it is the method of mathematical demonstration which consists in the logical deduction of the proposition to be proved from other propositions, previously established. Clearly, this procedure would involve an infinite regress unless some propositions were accepted without proof; such propositions are indeed found in every mathematical discipline which is rigorously developed;

* Reprinted from the *American Mathematical Monthly*, vol. 52, pp. 7–17 (1945). By courtesy of the Mathematical Association of America.

they are the *axioms* or *postulates* (we shall use these terms interchangeably) of the theory. Geometry provides the historically first example of the axiomatic presentation of a mathematical discipline. The classical set of postulates, however, on which Euclid based his system, has proved insufficient for the deduction of the well-known theorems of so-called euclidean geometry; it has therefore been revised and supplemented in modern times, and at present various adequate systems of postulates for euclidean geometry are available; the one most closely related to Euclid's system is probably that of Hilbert.

2. *The Inadequacy of Euclid's Postulates*

The inadequacy of Euclid's own set of postulates illustrates a point which is crucial for the axiomatic method in modern mathematics. Once the postulates for a theory have been laid down, every further proposition of the theory must be proved exclusively by logical deduction from the postulates; any appeal, explicit or implicit, to a feeling of self-evidence, or to the characteristics of geometrical figures, or to our experiences concerning the behavior of rigid bodies in physical space or the like, is strictly prohibited; such devices may have a heuristic value in guiding our efforts to find a strict proof for a theorem, but the proof itself must contain absolutely no reference to such aids. This is particularly important in geometry, where our so-called intuition of geometrical relationships, supported by reference to figures or to previous physical experiences, may induce us tacitly to make use of assumptions which are neither formulated in our postulates nor provable by means of them. Consider, for example, the theorem that in a triangle the three medians bisecting the sides intersect in one point which divides each of them in the ratio of $1:2$. To prove this theorem, one shows first that in any triangle ABC (see figure) the line segment MN which connects the centers of AB and AC is parallel to BC and therefore half as long as the latter side. Then the lines BN and CM are drawn, and an examination of the triangles MON and BOC leads to the proof of the theorem. In this procedure, it is usually taken for granted that BN and CM intersect in a point O which lies between B and N as well as between C and M. This assumption is based on geometrical intuition, and indeed, it cannot be deduced from Euclid's postulates; to make it strictly demonstrable and independent of any refer-

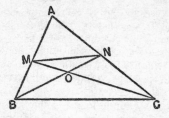

ence to intuition, a special group of postulates has been added to those of Euclid; they are the postulates of order. One of these—to give an example—asserts that if A, B, C are points on a straight line l, and if B lies between A and C, then B also lies between C and A.—Not even as "trivial" an assumption as this may be taken for granted; the system of postulates has to be made so complete that all the required propositions can be deduced from it by purely logical means.

Another illustration of the point under consideration is provided by the proposition that triangles which agree in two sides and the enclosed angle, are congruent. In Euclid's Elements, this proposition is presented as a theorem; the alleged proof, however, makes use of the ideas of motion and superimposition of figures and thus involves tacit assumptions which are based on our geometric intuition and on experiences with rigid bodies, but which are definitely not warranted by—*i.e.* deducible from—Euclid's postulates. In Hilbert's system, therefore, this proposition (more precisely: part of it) is explicitly included among the postulates.

3. *Mathematical Certainty*

It is this purely deductive character of mathematical proof which forms the basis of mathematical certainty: What the rigorous proof of a theorem—say the proposition about the sum of the angles in a triangle—establishes is not the truth of the proposition in question but rather a conditional insight to the effect that that proposition is certainly true *provided that* the postulates are true; in other words, the proof of a mathematical proposition establishes the fact that the latter is logically implied by the postulates of the theory in question. Thus, each mathematical theorem can be cast into the form

$$(P_1 \cdot P_2 \cdot P_3 \cdot \cdots \cdot P_N) \to T$$

where the expression on the left is the conjunction (joint assertion) of all the postulates, the symbol on the right represents the theorem in its customary formulation, and the arrow expresses the relation of logical implication or entailment. Precisely this character of mathematical theorems is the reason for their peculiar certainty and necessity, as I shall now attempt to show.

It is typical of any purely logical deduction that the conclusion to which it leads simply re-asserts (a proper or improper) part of what has already been stated in the premises. Thus, to illustrate this point by a very elementary example, from the premise, "This figure is a right triangle," we can deduce the conclusion, "This figure is a triangle"; but this conclusion clearly reiterates part of the information already contained in the premise. Again, from the premises, "All primes different from 2 are odd" and "n is a prime different from 2," we can infer logically that n is odd; but this consequence merely repeats part (indeed a relatively small part) of the information contained in the premises. The same situation prevails in all other cases of logical deduction; and we may, therefore, say that logical deduction—which is the one and only method of mathematical proof—is a technique of conceptual analysis: it discloses what assertions are concealed in a given set of premises, and it makes us realize to what we committed ourselves in accepting those premises; but none of the results obtained by this technique ever goes by one iota beyond the information already contained in the initial assumptions.

Since all mathematical proofs rest exclusively on logical deductions from certain postulates, it follows that a mathematical theorem, such as the Pythagorean theorem in geometry, asserts nothing that is *objectively* or *theoretically new* as compared with the postulates from which it is derived, although its content may well be *psychologically new* in the sense that we were not aware of its being implicitly contained in the postulates.

The nature of the peculiar certainty of mathematics is now clear: A mathematical theorem is certain *relatively* to the set of postulates from which it is derived; *i.e.* it is necessarily true *if* those postulates are true; and this is so because the theorem, if rigorously proved, simply re-asserts part of what has been stipulated in the postulates. A truth of this conditional type obviously implies no assertions about matters of empirical fact and can, therefore, never get into conflict with any empirical findings, even of the most unexpected kind; consequently, unlike the hypotheses and theories of empirical science, it can never suffer the fate of being disconfirmed by new evidence: A mathematical truth is irrefutably certain just because it is devoid of factual, or empirical content. Any theorem of geometry, therefore, when cast into the conditional form described earlier, is analytic in the technical sense of logic, and thus true *a priori*; *i.e.* its truth can be established by means of the formal machinery of logic alone, without any reference to empirical data.

4. Postulates and Truth

Now it might be felt that our analysis of geometrical truth so far tells only half of the relevant story. For while a geometrical proof no doubt enables us to assert a proposition conditionally—namely on condition that the postulates are accepted—, is it not correct to add that geometry also unconditionally asserts the truth of its postulates and thus, by virtue of the deductive relationship between postulates and theorems, enables us unconditionally to assert the truth of its theorems? Is it not an unconditional assertion of geometry that two points determine one and only one straight line that connects them, or that in any triangle, the sum of the angles equals two right angles? That this is definitely not the case, is evidenced by two important aspects of the axiomatic treatment of geometry which will now be briefly considered.

The first of these features is the well-known fact that in the more recent development of mathematics, several systems of geometry have been constructed which are incompatible with euclidean geometry, and in which, for example, the two propositions just mentioned do not necessarily hold. Let us briefly recollect some of the basic facts concerning these *noneuclidean geometries*. The postulates on which euclidean geometry rests include the famous postulate of the parallels, which, in the case of plane geometry, asserts in effect that through every point P not on a given line l there exists exactly one parallel to l, *i.e.*, one straight line which does not meet l. As this postulate is considerably less simple than the others, and as it was also felt to be intuitively less plausible than the latter, many efforts were made in the history of geometry to prove that this proposition need not be accepted as an axiom, but that it can be deduced as a theorem from the remaining body of postulates. All attempts in this direction failed, however; and finally it was conclusively demonstrated that a proof of the parallel principle on the basis of the other postulates of euclidean geometry (even in its modern, completed form) is impossible. This was shown by proving that a perfect self-consistent geometrical theory is obtained if the postulate of the parallels is replaced by the assumption that through any point P not on a given straight line l there exist at least two parallels to l. This postulate obviously contradicts the euclidean postulate of the parallels, and if the latter were actually a consequence of the other postulates of euclidean geometry, then the new set of postulates would clearly involve a contradiction, which can be shown not to be the case. This first non-euclidean type of geometry, which is called hyperbolic geometry, was discovered in the early 20's of the last century almost simultaneously, but independently by the Russian N. I. Lobachevsky, and by the Hungarian J. Bolyai. Later, Riemann developed an alternative geometry, known as elliptical geometry, in which the axiom of the parallels is replaced by the postulate that no line has any parallels. (The acceptance of this postulate, however, in contradistinction to that of hyperbolic geometry, requires the modification of some further axioms of euclidean geometry, if a consistent new theory is to result.) As is to be expected, many of the theorems of these non-euclidean geometries are at variance with those of euclidean theory; thus, *e.g.*, in the hyperbolic geometry of two dimensions, there exist, for each straight line l, through any point P not on l, infinitely many straight lines which do not meet l; also, the sum of the angles in any triangle is less than two right angles. In elliptic geometry, this angle sum is always greater than two right angles; no two straight lines are parallel; and while two different points usually determine exactly one straight line connecting them (as they always do in euclidean geometry), there are certain pairs of points which are connected by infinitely many different straight lines. An illustration of this latter type of geometry is provided by the geometrical structure of that curved two-dimensional space which is represented by the surface of a sphere, when the concept of straight line is interpreted by that of great circle on the sphere. In this space, there are no parallel lines since any two great circles intersect; the endpoints of any diameter of the sphere are points connected by infinitely many different "straight lines," and the sum of the angles in a triangle is always in excess of two right angles. Also, in this space, the ratio between the circumference and the diameter of a circle (not necessarily a great circle) is always less than 2π.

Elliptic and hyperbolic geometry are not the only types of non-euclidean geometry; various other types have been developed; we shall later have occasion to refer to a much more general form of non-euclidean geometry which was likewise devised by Riemann.

The fact that these different types of geometry have been developed in modern mathematics shows clearly that mathematics cannot be said to assert the truth of any particular set of geometrical postulates; all that pure mathematics is interested in, and all that it can establish, is the deductive consequences of given sets of postulates and thus the necessary truth of the ensuing theorems relatively to the postulates under consideration.

A second observation which likewise shows that mathematics does not assert the truth of any particular set of postulates refers to *the status of the concepts in geometry*. There exists, in every axiomatized theory, a close parallelism between the treatment of the propositions and that of the concepts of the system. As we have seen, the propositions fall into two classes: the postulates, for which no proof is given, and the theorems, each of which has to be derived from the postulates. Analogously, the concepts fall into two classes: the primitive or basic concepts, for which no definition is given, and the others, each of which has to be precisely defined in terms of the primitives. (The admission of some undefined concepts is clearly necessary if an infinite regress in definition is to be avoided.) The analogy goes farther: Just as there exists an infinity of theoretically suitable axiom systems for one and the same theory—say, euclidean geometry—so there also exists an infinity of theoretically possible choices for the primitive terms of that theory; very often—but not always— different axiomatizations of the same theory involve not only different postulates, but also different sets of primitives. Hilbert's axiomatization of plane geometry contains six primitives: point, straight line, incidence (of a point on a line), betweenness (as a relation of three points on a straight line), congruence for line segments, and congruence for angles. (Solid geometry, in Hilbert's axiomatization, requires two further primitives, that of plane and that of incidence of a point on a plane.) All other concepts of geometry, such as those of angle, triangle, circle, *etc.*, are defined in terms of these basic concepts.

But if the primitives are not defined within geometrical theory, what meaning are we to assign to them? The answer is that it is entirely unnecessary to connect any particular meaning with them. True, the words "point," "straight line," *etc.*, carry definite connotations with them which relate to the familiar geometrical figures, but the validity of the propositions is completely independent of these connotations. Indeed, suppose that in axiomatized euclidean geometry, we replace the over-suggestive terms "point," "straight line," "incidence," "betweenness," *etc.*, by the neutral terms "object of kind 1," "object of kind 2," "relation No. 1," "relation No. 2," *etc.*, and suppose that we present this modified wording of geometry to a competent mathematician or logician who, however, knows nothing of the customary connotations of the primitive terms. For this logician, all proofs would clearly remain valid, for as we saw before, a rigorous proof in geometry rests on deduction from the axioms alone without any reference to the customary interpretation of the various geometrical concepts used. We see therefore that indeed no specific meaning has to be attached to the primitive terms of an axiomatized theory; and in a precise logical presentation of axiomatized geometry the primitive concepts are accordingly treated as so-called logical variables.

As a consequence, geometry cannot be said to assert the truth of its postulates, since the latter are formulated in terms of concepts without any specific meaning; indeed, for this very reason, the postulates themselves do not make any specific assertion which could possibly be called true or false! In the terminology of modern logic, the postulates are not sentences, but sentential functions with the primitive concepts as variable arguments. This point also shows that the postulates of geometry cannot be considered as "self-evident truths," because where no assertion is made, no self-evidence can be claimed.

5. *Pure and Physical Geometry*

Geometry thus construed is a purely formal discipline; we shall refer to it also as *pure geometry*. A pure geometry, then, —no matter whether it is of the euclidean or of a non-euclidean variety—deals with no specific subject-matter; in particular, it asserts nothing about physical space. All its theorems are analytic and thus true with certainty precisely because they are devoid of factual content. Thus, to characterize the import of pure geometry, we might use the standard form of a movie-disclaimer: No portrayal of the characteristics of geometrical figures or of the spatial properties or relationships of actual physical bodies is intended, and any similarities between the primitive concepts and their customary geometrical connotations are purely coincidental.

But just as in the case of some motion pictures, so in the case at least of euclidean geometery, the disclaimer does not sound quite convincing: Historically speaking, at least, euclidean geometry has its origin in the generalization and systematization of certain empirical discoveries which were made in connection with the measurement of areas and volumes, the practice of surveying, and the development of astronomy. Thus understood, geometry has factual import; it is an empirical science which might be called, in very general terms, the theory of the structure of physical space, or briefly, *physical geometry*. What is the relation between pure and physical geometry?

When the physicist uses the concepts of point, straight line, incidence, *etc.*, in statements about physical objects, he obviously connects with each of them a more or less definite physical meaning. Thus, the term "point" serves to designate points, *i.e.*, objects of the kind illustrated by pin-points, cross hairs, *etc.* Similarly, the term "straight line" refers to straight lines in the sense of physics, such as illustrated by taut strings or by the path of light rays in a homogeneous medium. Analogously, each of the other geometrical concepts has a concrete physical meaning in the statements of physical geometry. In view of this situation, we can say that physical geometry is obtained by what is called, in contemporary logic, a semantical interpretation of pure geometry. Generally speaking, a semantical interpretation of a pure mathematical theory, whose primitives are not assigned any specific meaning, consists in giving each primitive (and thus, indirectly, each defined term) a specific meaning or designatum. In the case of physical geometry, this meaning is physical in the sense just illustrated; it is possible, however, to assign a purely arithmetical meaning to each concept of geometry; the possibility of such an arithmetical interpretation of geometry is of great importance in the study of the consistency and other logical characteristics of geometry, but it falls outside the scope of the present discussion.

By virtue of the physical interpretation of the originally uninterpreted primitives of a geometrical theory, physical meaning is indirectly assigned also to every defined concept of the theory; and if every geometrical term is now taken in its physical interpretation, then every postulate and every theorem of the theory under consideration turns into a statement of physics, with respect to which the question as to truth or falsity may meaningfully be raised—a circumstance which clearly contradistinguishes the propositions of physical geometry from those of the corresponding uninterpreted pure theory. Consider, for example, the following postulate of pure euclidean geometry: For any two objects x, y of kind 1, there exists exactly one object l of kind 2 such that both x and y stand in relation No. 1 to l. As long as the three primitives occurring in this postulate are uninterpreted, it is obviously meaningless to ask whether the postulate is true. But by virtue of the above physical interpretation, the postulate turns into the following statement: For any two physical points x, y there exists exactly one physical straight line l such that both x and y lie on l. But this is a physical hypothesis, and we may now meaningfully ask whether it is true or false. Similarly, the theorem about the sum of the angles in a triangle turns into the assertion that the sum of the angles (in the physical sense) of a figure bounded by the paths of three light rays equals two right angles.

Thus, the physical interpretation transforms a given pure geometrical theory—euclidean or non-euclidean—into a system of physical hypotheses which, if true, might be said to constitute a theory of the structure of physical space. But the question whether a given geometrical theory in physical interpretation is factually correct represents a problem not of pure mathematics but of empirical science; it has to be settled on the basis of suitable experiments or systematic observations. The only assertion the mathematician can make in this context is this: If all the postulates of a given geometry, in their physical interpretation, are true, then all the theorems of that geometry, in their physical interpretation, are necessarily true, too, since they are logically deducible from the postulates. It might seem, therefore, that in order to decide whether physical space is euclidean or non-euclidean in structure, all that we have to do is to test the respective postulates in their physical interpretation. However, this is not directly feasible; here, as in the case of any other physical theory, the basic hypotheses are largely incapable of a direct experimental test; in geometry, this is particularly obvious for such postulates as the parallel axiom or Cantor's axiom of continuity in Hilbert's system of euclidean geometry, which makes an assertion about certain infinite sets of points on a straight line. Thus, the empirical test of a physical geometry no less than that of any other scientific theory has to proceed indirectly; namely, by deducing from the basic hypotheses of the theory certain consequences, or predictions, which are amenable to an experimental test. If a test bears out a prediction, then it constitutes confirming evidence (though, of course, no conclusive proof) for the theory; otherwise, it disconfirms the theory. If an adequate amount of confirming evidence for a theory has been established, and if no disconfirming evidence has been found, then the theory may be accepted by the scientist "until further notice."

It is in the context of this indirect procedure that pure mathematics and logic acquire their inestimable importance for empirical science: While formal logic and pure mathematics do not in themselves establish any assertions about matters of empirical fact, they provide an efficient and entirely indispensable machinery for deducing, from abstract theoretical assumptions, such as the laws of Newtonian mechanics or the postulates of euclidean geometry in physical interpretation, consequences concrete and specific enough to be accessible to direct experimental test. Thus, *e.g.*, pure euclidean geometry shows that from its postulates there may be deduced the theorem about the sum of the angles in a triangle, and that this deduction is possible no matter how the basic concepts of geometry are interpreted; hence also in the case of the physical interpretation of euclidean geometry. This theorem, in its physical interpretation, is accessible to experimental test; and since the postulates of elliptic and of hyperbolic geometry imply values different from two right angles for the angle sum of a triangle, this particular proposition seems to afford a good opportunity for a crucial experiment. And no less a mathematician than Gauss did indeed perform this test; by means of optical methods—and thus using the interpretation of physical straight lines as paths of light rays—he ascertained the angle sum of a large triangle determined by three mountain tops. Within the limits of experimental error, he found it equal to two right angles.

6. On Poincaré's Conventionalism Concerning Geometry

But suppose that Gauss had found a noticeable deviation from this value; would that have meant a refutation of euclidean geometry in its physical interpretation, or, in other words, of the hypothesis that physical space is euclidean in structure? Not necessarily; for the deviation might have been accounted for by a hypothesis to the effects that the paths of the light rays involved in the sighting process were bent by some disturbing force and thus were not actually straight lines. The same kind of reference to deforming forces could also be used if, say, the euclidean theorems of congruence for plane figures were tested in their physical interpretation by means of experiments involving rigid bodies, and if any violations of the theorems were found. This point is by no means trivial; Henri Poincaré, the great French mathematician and theoretical physicist, based on considerations of this type his famous *conventionalism concerning geometry*. It was his opinion that no empirical test, whatever its outcome, can conclusively invalidate the euclidean conception of physical space; in other words, the validity of euclidean geometry in physical science can always be preserved—if necessary, by suitable changes in the theories of physics, such as the introduction of new hypotheses concerning deforming or defecting forces. Thus, the question as to whether physical space has a euclidean or a non-euclidean structure would become a matter of convention, and the decision to preserve euclidean geometry at all costs would recommend itself, according to Poincaré, by the greater simplicity of euclidean as compared with non-euclidean geometrical theory.

It appears, however, that Poincaré's account is an oversimplification. It rightly calls attention to the fact that the test of a physical geometry G always presupposes a certain body P of non-geometrical physical hypotheses (including the physical theory of the instruments of measurement and observation used in the test), and that the so-called test of G actually bears on the combined theoretical system $G \cdot P$ rather than on G alone. Now, if predictions derived from $G \cdot P$ are contradicted by experimental findings, then a change in the theoretical structure becomes necessary. In classical physics, *G* always was euclidean geometry in its physical interpretation, *GE;* and when experimental evidence required a modification of the theory, it was *P* rather than *GE* which was changed. But Poincaré's assertion that this procedure would always be distinguished by its greater simplicity is not entirely correct; for what has to be taken into consideration is the simplicity of the total system *G·P,* and not just that of its geometrical part. And here it is clearly conceivable that a simpler total theory in accordance with all the relevant empirical evidence is obtainable by going over to a non-euclidean form of geometry rather than by preserving the euclidean structure of physical space and making adjustments only in part *P.*

And indeed, just this situation has arisen in physics in connection with the development of the general theory of relativity: If the primitive terms of geometry are given physical interpretations along the lines indicated before, then certain findings in astronomy represent good evidence in favor of a total physical theory with a non-euclidean geometry as part *G.* According to this theory, the physical universe at large is a three-dimensional curved space of a very complex geometrical structure; it is finite in volume and yet unbounded in all directions. However, in comparatively small areas, such as those involved in Gauss' experiment, euclidean geometry can serve as a good approximative account of the geometrical structure of space. The kind of structure ascribed to physical space in this theory may be illustrated by an analogue in two dimensions; namely, the surface of a sphere. The geometrical structure of the latter, as was pointed out before, can be described by means of elliptic geomtry, if the primitive term "straight line" is interpreted as meaning "great circle," and if the other primitives are given analogous interpretations. In this sense, the surface of a sphere is a two-dimensional curved space of non-euclidean structure, whereas the plane is a two-dimensional space of euclidean structure. While the plane is unbounded in all directions, and infinite in size, the spherical surface is finite in size and yet unbounded in all directions: a two-dimensional physicist, travelling along "straight lines" of that space would never encounter any boundaries of his space; instead he would finally return to his point of departure, provided that his life span and his technical facilities were sufficient for such a trip in consideration of the size of his "universe." It is interesting to note that the physicists of that world, even if they lacked any intuition of a three-dimensional space, could empirically ascertain the fact that their two-dimensional space was curved. This might be done by means of the method of traveling along straight lines; another, simpler test would consist in determining the angle sum in a triangle; again another in determining, by means of measuring tapes, the ratio of the circumference of a circle (not necessarily a great circle) to its diameter; this ratio would turn out to be less than π.

The geometrical structure which relativity physics ascribes to physical space is a three-dimensional analogue to that of the surface of a sphere, or, to be more exact, to that of the closed and finite surface of a potato, whose curvature varies from point to point. In our physical universe, the curvature of space at a given point is determined by the distribution of masses in its neighborhood; near large masses such as the sun, space is strongly curved, while in regions of low mass-density, the structure of the universe is approximately euclidean. The hypothesis stating the connection between the mass distribution and the curvature of space at a point has been approximately confirmed by astronomical observations concerning the paths of light rays in the gravitational field of the sun.

The geometrical theory which is used to describe the structure of the physical universe is of a type that may be characterized as a generalization of elliptic geometry. It was originally constructed by Riemann as a purely mathematical theory, without any concrete possibility of practical application at hand. When Einstein, in developing his general theory of relativity, looked for an appropriate mathematical theory to deal with the structure of physical space, he found in Riemann's abstract system the conceptual tool he needed. This fact throws an interesting sidelight on the importance for sicentific progress of that type of investigation which the "practical-minded" man in the street tends to dismiss as useless, abstract mathematical speculation.

Of course, a geometrical theory in physical interpretation can never be validated with mathematical certainty, no matter how extensive the experimental tests to which it is subjected; like any other theory of empirical science, it can acquire only a more or less high degree of confirmation. Indeed, the considerations presented in this article show that the demand for mathematical certainty in empirical matters is misguided and unreasonable; for, as we saw, mathematical certainty of knowledge can be attained only at the price of analyticity and thus of complete lack of factual content. Let me summarize this insight in Einstein's words:

"As far as the laws of mathematics refer to reality, they are not certain; and as far as they are certain, they do not refer to reality."

CRISES IN THE FOUNDATIONS
OF MATHEMATICS

HOWARD EVES and CARROLL V. NEWSOM

What is today known as metamathematics originated in the pioneer work of such men as Cantor, Hilbert, Frege, Brouwer, Whitehead, Russell, Carnap and Gödel, to mention only a few of the outstanding thinkers.

Perhaps the most crucial concept involved in mathematical philosophy is the relation of finitude to infinitude. At all events, mathematical philosophy, at the present moment in the history of human thought, has once more come face to face with seemingly unresolvable dilemmas. These are most ably discussed here by Professors Eves and Newsom. It is hoped that the reader will not feel completely frustrated, since it is probably safe to say that mathematicians themselves, while somewhat disconcerted for the time being, are by no means deterred from continuing their search for "the eternal verities."

Crises in the Foundations of Mathematics*

A STUDY of the history of mathematics from Greek antiquity to the present reveals that the foundations of mathematics have undergone three profoundly disturbing crises.

The first crisis in the foundations of mathematics arose in the fifth century B.C., and, indeed, such a crisis could not have occurred much earlier, for, as we have seen, mathematics as a deductive study originated not earlier than the sixth century B.C., perhaps with Thales, Pythagoras, and their pupils. The crisis was precipitated by the unexpected discovery that not all geometrical magnitudes of the same kind are commensurable with one another; it was shown, for example, that the diagonal and side of a square contain no common unit of measure. Since the Pythagorean development of magnitudes was built upon the firm intuitive belief that all like magnitudes are commensurable, the discovery that like magnitudes may be incommensurable proved to be highly devastating. For instance, the entire Pythagorean theory of proportion with all of its consequences had to be scrapped as unsound. The resolution of this first crisis in the foundations of mathematics was neither easily nor quickly realized. It was finally achieved in about 370 B.C. by the brilliant Eudoxus, whose revised theory of magnitude and proportion is one of the great mathematical masterpieces of all time. Eudoxus' remarkable treatment of incommensurables may be found in the fifth book of Euclid's *Elements;* it coincides essentially with the modern exposition of irrational numbers that was given by Richard Dedekind in 1872. . . .

The second crisis in the foundations of mathematics followed the discovery of the calculus by Newton and Leibniz in the late seventeenth century.[1] We have seen how the successors of these men, intoxicated by the power and applicability of the new tool, failed to consider sufficiently the solidity of the base upon which the subject was founded, so that instead of having demonstrations justify results, results were used to

* Reprinted from Howard Eves and Carroll Newsom, *An Introduction to the Foundations and Fundamental Concepts of Mathematics,* 1958, pp. 281–291. By permission and courtesy of Holt, Rinehart and Winston, Inc.

justify demonstrations. With the passage of time, contradictions and paradoxes arose in increasing numbers, and a serious crisis in the foundations of mathematics became evident. It was realized more and more that the edifice of analysis was being built upon sand, and finally, in the early nineteenth century, Cauchy took the first steps toward resolving the crisis by replacing the hazy method of infinitesimals by the precise method of limits. With the subsequent so-called arithmetization of analysis by Weierstrass and his followers, it was felt that the second crisis in the foundations of mathematics had been overcome, and that the whole structure of mathematics had been redeemed and placed upon an unimpeachable base....

The third crisis in the foundations of mathematics materialized with shocking suddenness in 1897, and, though now well over half a century old, is still not resolved to the satisfaction of all concerned. The crisis was brought about by the discovery of paradoxes or antinomies in the fringe of Cantor's general theory of sets. Since so much of mathematics is permeated with set concepts and, for that matter, can actually be made to rest upon set theory as a foundation, the discovery of paradoxes in set theory naturally cast into doubt the validity of the whole foundational structure of mathematics.

In 1897 the Italian mathematician, Burali-Forti, brought to light the first publicized paradox of set theory. . . . The essence of the paradox can be given by a nontechnical description of a very similar paradox found by Cantor two years later. In his theory of sets, Cantor had succeeded in proving that for any given transfinite number there is always a greater transfinite number, so that just as there is no greatest natural number, there also is no greatest transfinite number. Now consider the set whose members are all possible sets. Surely no set can have more members than this set of all sets. But if this is the case, how can there be a transfinite number greater than the transfinite number of this set?

Whereas the Burali-Forti and Cantor paradoxes involve results of set theory, Bertrand Russell discovered in 1902 a paradox depending on nothing more than just the concept of set itself. Before describing the Russell paradox, we note that sets either are members of themselves or are not members of themselves. Thus the set of all abstract ideas is itself an abstract idea, but the set of all men is not a man. Again, the set of all sets is itself a set, but the set of all stars is not a star. Let us represent the set of all sets which are members of themselves by M, and the set of all sets which are not members of themselves by N. We now ask ourselves whether set N is or is not a member of itself. If N is a member of itself, then N is a member of M and not of N, and N is not a member of itself. On the other hand, if N is not a member of itself, then N is a member of N and not of M, and N is a member of itself. The paradox lies in the fact that in either case we are led to a contradiction. . . .

The Russell paradox has been popularized in many forms. One of the best known of these forms was given by Russell himself in 1919 and concerns the plight of the barber of a certain village who has enunciated the principle that he shaves all those persons and only those persons of the village who do not shave themselves. The paradoxical nature of this situation is realized when we try to answer the question, "Does the barber shave himself?" If he does shave himself, then he shouldn't according to his principle; if he doesn't shave himself, then he should according to his principle.

Since the discovery of the above contradictions within Cantor's theory of sets, additional paradoxes have been produced in abundance. These modern paradoxes of set theory are related to several ancient paradoxes of logic. For example, Eubulides, of the fourth century B.C., is credited with making the remark, "This statement I am now making is false." If Eubulides' statement is true, then, by what it says, the statement must be false. On the other hand, if Eubulides' statement is false, then it follows that his statement must be true. Thus Eubulides' statement can neither be true nor false without entailing a contradiction. Still older than the Eubulides paradox may be the unauthenticated Epimenides paradox. Epimenides, who himself was a Cretan philosopher of the sixth century B.C., is claimed to have made the remark, "Cretans are always liars." A simple analysis of this remark easily reveals that it, too, is self-contradictory.

The existence of paradoxes in set theory, like those described above, clearly indicates that something is wrong. Since their discovery, a great deal of literature on the subject has appeared, and numerous attempts at a solution have been offered.

So far as mathematics is concerned, there seems to be an easy way out. One has merely to reconstruct set theory on an axiomatic basis sufficiently restrictive to exclude the known antinomies. The first such attempt was made by Zermelo in

1908, and subsequent refinements have been made by Fraenkel (1922, 1925), Skolem (1922, 1929), von Neumann (1925, 1928), Bernays (1937–1948), and others. But such a procedure has been criticized as merely avoiding the paradoxes; certainly it does not explain them. Moreover, this procedure carries no guarantee that other kinds of paradoxes will not crop up in the future.

There is another procedure which apparently both explains and avoids the known paradoxes. If examined carefully, it will be seen that each of the paradoxes considered above involves a set S and a member m of S whose definition depends upon S. Such a definition is said to be *impredicative*, and impredicative definitions are, in a sense, circular. Consider, for instance, Russell's barber paradox. Let us designate the barber by m and the set of all members of the barber's village by S. Then m is defined impredicatively as "that member of S who shaves all those members and only those members of S who do not shave themselves." The circular nature of this definition is evident—the definition of the barber involves the members of the village and the barber himself is a member of the village.

Poincaré considered the cause of the antinomies to lie in impredicative definitions, and Russell expressed the same view in his Vicious Circle Principle: *No set S is allowed to contain members m definable only in terms of S, or members m involving or presupposing S.* This principle amounts to a restriction on the concept of set. Cantor had attempted to give the concept of set a very general meaning by stating: *By a set S we are to understand any collection into a whole of definite and separate objects m of our intuition or our thought; these objects m are called the elements of S.* The theory of sets constructed on Cantor's general concept of set leads, as we have seen, to contradictions, but if the notion of set is restricted by the Vicious Circle Principle, the resulting theory avoids the known antinomies. The outlawing of impredicative definitions would appear, then, to be a solution to the known paradoxes of set theory. There is, however, one serious objection to this solution; namely, there are parts of mathematics, which mathematicians are very reluctant to discard, that contain impredicative definitions. . . .

Other attempts to solve the paradoxes of set theory look for the trouble in logic, and it must be admitted that the discovery of the paradoxes in the unrestricted theory of sets has brought about a thorough investigation of the foundations of logic. Very intriguing is the suggestion that the way out of the difficulties of the paradoxes may be through the use of a three-valued logic. For example, in the Russell paradox given above, we saw that the statement, "N is a member of itself," can be neither true nor false. Here a third possibility would be helpful, and the situation would be saved if we could simply classify the statement as ?.

There have arisen three main philosophies, or schools of thought, concerning the foundations of mathematics—the so-called logistic, intuitionist, and formalist schools. Naturally, any modern philosophy of the foundations of mathematics must, somehow or other, cope with the present crisis in the foundations of mathematics. In the next section we shall very briefly consider these three schools of thought and shall point out how each proposes to deal with the antinomies of general set theory.

A philosophy may be regarded as an explanation which attempts to make some kind of sense out of the natural disorder of a set of experiences. From this point of view it is possible to have a philosophy of almost anything—a philosophy of art, of life, of religion, of education, of society, of history, of science, of mathematics, even of philosophy itself. A philosophy amounts to a process of refining and ordering experiences and values; it seeks relations among things which are normally felt to be disparate, and finds important differences between things normally confused as the same; it is the description of a theory concerning the nature of something. In particular, a philosophy of mathematics essentially amounts to an attempted reconstruction in which the chaotic mass of mathematical knowledge accumulated over the ages is given a certain sense or order. Clearly, a philosophy is a function of time, and a particular philosophy may become outdated or have to be altered in the light of additional experiences. We are here concerned with only contemporary philosophies of mathematics—philosophies which take account of the recent advances in mathematics and of the current crisis in the subject.

There are three principal present-day philosophies of mathematics, each of which has attracted a sizable group of adherents and developed a large body of associated literature. These are referred to as the logistic school, of which Russell and Whitehead are the chief expositors; the intuitionist school, led by Brouwer; and the formalist school, developed principally by Hilbert. There are, of course, present-day philosophies of mathematics other than these three. There are some independent philosophies and some which constitute various mixtures of the principal three, but these other points of view have not been so widely cultivated, or do not comprise a reconstruction of mathematics of similar extent.

In this section we shall attempt a description of each of these three principal philosophies of mathematics. Obviously, it will not be possible . . . to do proper justice to this subject, but it is hoped that the treatment will be sufficient to give some idea of these current schools of thought which are so intimately connected with the foundations and fundamental concepts of mathematics.

(1) *Logicism*

The logistic thesis is that mathematics is a branch of logic. Rather than being just a tool of mathematics, logic becomes the progenitor of mathematics. All mathematical concepts are to be formulated in terms of logical concepts, and all theorems of mathematics are to be developed as theorems of logic; the distinction between mathematics and logic becomes merely one of practical convenience.

The notion of logic as a science containing the principles and ideas underlying all other sciences dates back at least as far as Leibniz (1666). The actual reduction of mathematical concepts to logical concepts was engaged in by Dedekind (1888) and Frege (1884–1903), and the statement of mathematical theorems by means of a logical symbolism was undertaken by Peano (1889–1908). These men, then, are forerunners of the logistic school, which received its definitive expression in the monumental *Principia Mathematica* of Whitehead and Russell (1910–1913). This great and complex work purports to be a detailed reduction of the whole of mathematics to logic. Subsequent modifications and refinements of the program have been supplied by Wittgenstein (1922), Chwistek (1924–1925), Ramsey, (1926), Langford (1927), Carnap (1931), Quine (1940), and others.

The logistic thesis arises naturally from the efforts to push down the foundations of mathematics to as deep a level as possible. We have seen how these foundations were established in the real number system, and then how they were pushed back from the real number system to the natural number system, and thence into set theory. Since the theory of classes is an essential part of logic, the idea of reducing mathematics to logic certainly suggests itself. The logistic thesis is thus an attempted synthesization suggested by an important trend in the history of the application of the mathematical method.

The *Principia Mathematica* starts with "primitive ideas" and "primitive propositions," corresponding to the "undefined terms" and "postulates" of a formal abstract development. These primitive ideas and propositions are not to be subjected to interpretation but are restricted to intuitive concepts of logic; they are to be regarded as, or at least are to be accepted as, plausible descriptions and hypotheses concerning the real world. In short, a concrete rather than an abstract point of view prevails, and consequently no attempt is made to prove the consistency of the primitive propositions. The aim of *Principia Mathematica* is to develop mathematical concepts and theorems from these primitive ideas and propositions, starting with a calculus of propositions, proceeding up through the theory of classes and relations to the establishment of the natural number system, and thence to all mathematics derivable from the natural number system. In this development the natural numbers emerge with the unique meanings which we ordinarily assign to them and are not nonuniquely defined as *any things* which satisfy a certain set of abstract postulates.

To avoid the contradictions of set theory, *Principia Mathematica* employs a "theory of types." Somewhat oversimply described, such a theory sets up a hierarchy of levels of elements. The primary elements constitute those of type 0; classes of elements of type 0 constitute those of type 1; classes of elements of type 1 constitute those of type 2; and so on. In applying the theory of types, one follows the rule that all the elements of any class must be of the same type. Adherence to this rule precludes impredicative definitions and thus avoids the paradoxes of set theory. As originally presented in *Principia Mathematica*, hierarchies within hierarchies appeared, leading to the so-called "ramified" theory of types. In order to obtain the impredicative definitions needed to establish analysis, an "axiom of reducibility" had to be introduced. The nonprimitive and arbitrary character of this axiom drew forth severe criticism, and much of the subsequent refinement of the logistic program lies in attempts to devise some method of avoiding the disliked axiom of reducibility.

Whether or not the logistic thesis has been established seems to be a matter of opinion. Although some accept the program as satisfactory, others have found many objections to it. For one thing, the logistic thesis can be questioned on the ground that the systematic development of logic (as of any organized study) presupposes mathematical ideas in its formulation, such as the fundamental idea of iteration which must be used, for example, in describing the theory of types or the idea of deduction from given premises.

(2) Intuitionism

The intuitionist thesis is that mathematics is to be built solely by finite constructive methods on the intuitively given sequence of natural numbers. According to this view, then, at the very base of mathematics lies a primitive intuition, allied, no doubt, to our temporal sense of before and after, which allows us to conceive a single object, then one more, then one more, and so on endlessly. In this way we obtain unending sequences, the best known of which is the sequence of natural numbers. From this intuitive base of the sequence of natural numbers, any other mathematical object must be built in a purely constructive manner, employing a finite number of steps or operations. In the intuitionist thesis we have the genetical development of mathematics pushed to its extreme.

The intuitionist school (as a school) originated about 1908 with the Dutch mathematician L. E. J. Brouwer, although one finds some of the intuitionist ideas uttered earlier by such men as Kronecker (in the 1880's) and Poincaré (1902–1906). The school has gradually strengthened with the passage of time, has won over some eminent present-day mathematicians, and has exerted a tremendous influence on all thinking concerning the foundations of mathematics.

Some of the consequences of the intuitionist thesis are little short of revolutionary. Thus the insistence on constructive methods leads to a conception of mathematical existence not shared by all practicing mathematicians. For the intuitionists, an entity whose existence is to be proved must be shown to be constructible in a finite number of steps; it is not sufficient to show that the assumption of the entity's nonexistence leads to a contradiction. This means that many existence proofs found in current mathematics are not acceptable to the intuitionists.

An important instance of the intuitionists' insistence upon constructive procedures is in the theory of sets. For the intuitionists, a set cannot be thought of as a ready-made collection, but must be considered as a law by means of which the elements of the set can be constructed in a step-by-step fashion. This concept of set rules out the possibility of such contradictory sets as "the set of all sets."

There is another remarkable consequence of the intuitionists' insistence upon finite constructibility, and this is the denial of the universal acceptance of the law of excluded middle! Consider, for example, the number x, which is defined to be $(-1)^k$, where k is the number of the first decimal place in the decimal expansion of π where the sequence of consecutive digits 123456789 begins, and, if no such k exists, $x = 0$. Now, although the number x is well-defined, we cannot at the moment, under the intuitionists' restrictions, say that the proposition "$x = 0$" is either true or false. This proposition can be said to be true only when a proof of it has been constructed in a finite number of steps, and it can be said to be false only when a proof of this situation has been constructed in a finite number of steps. Until one or the other of these proofs is constructed, the proposition is neither true nor false, and the law of excluded middle is inapplicable. If, however, k is further restricted to be less than 5000, say, then it is perfectly correct to say that the proposition is now either true or false, for, with $k < 5000$, the truth or falseness can certainly be established in a finite number of steps.

Thus, for the intuitionists, the law of excluded middle holds for finite sets but should not be employed when dealing with infinite sets. This state of affairs is blamed by Brouwer on the sociological development of logic. The laws of logic emerged at a time in man's evolution when he had a good language for dealing with finite sets of phenomena; he then later made the mistake of applying these laws to the infinite sets of mathematics, with the result that antinomies arose.

In the *Principia Mathematica*, the law of excluded middle and the law of contradiction are equivalent. For the intuitionists, this situation no longer prevails, and it is an interesting problem to try, if possible, to set up the logical apparatus to which intuitionist ideas lead us. This was done in 1930 by A. Heyting, who succeeded in developing an intuitionist symbolic logic. Intuitionist mathematics thus produces its own type of logic, and mathematical logic, as a consequence, is a branch of mathematics.

There is the final important question: How much of existing mathematics can be built within the intuitionistic restrictions? If all of it can be so rebuilt, without too great an

increase in the labor required, then the present problem of
the foundations of mathematics would appear to be solved.
Now the intuitionists have succeeded in rebuilding large parts
of present-day mathematics, including a theory of the con-
tinuum and a set theory, but there is a great deal that is still
wanting. So far, intuitionist mathematics has turned out to be
considerably less powerful than classical mathematics, and in
many ways it is much more complicated to develop. This is
the fault found with the intuitionist approach—too much that
is dear to most mathematicians is sacrificed. This situation
may not exist forever, because there remains the possibility of
an intuitionist reconstruction of classical mathematics carried
out in a different and more successful way. And meanwhile,
in spite of present objections raised against the intuitionist
thesis, it is generally conceded that its methods do not lead
to contradictions.

(3) *Formalism*

The formalist thesis is that mathematics is concerned with
formal symbolic systems. In fact, mathematics is regarded
as a collection of such abstract developments, in which the
terms are mere symbols and the statements are formulas involving these symbols; the ultimate base of mathematics does
not lie in logic but only in a collection of prelogical marks
or symbols and in a set of operations with these marks. Since,
from this point of view, mathematics is devoid of concrete
content and contains only ideal symbolic elements, the
establishment of the consistency of the various branches of
mathematics becomes an important and necessary part of the
formalist program. Without such an accompanying consistency
proof, the whole study is essentially senseless. In the formalist
thesis we have the axiomatic development of mathematics
pushed to its extreme.

The formalist school was founded by David Hilbert after
completing his postulational study of geometry. In his *Grundlagen der Geometrie* (1899), Hilbert had sharpened the
mathematical method from the material axiomatics of Euclid
to the formal axiomatics of the present day. The formalist
point of view was developed later by Hilbert to meet the crisis
caused by the paradoxes of set theory and the challenge to
classical mathematics caused by intuitionistic criticism. Although Hilbert talked in formalistic terms as early as 1904,
not until after 1920 did he and his collaborators, Bernays,

Ackermann, von Neumann, and others, seriously start work on what is now known as the formalist program.

The success or failure of Hilbert's program to save classical mathematics hinges upon the solution of the consistency problem. Freedom from contradiction is guaranteed only by consistency proofs, and the older consistency proofs based upon interpretations and models usually merely shift the question of consistency from one domain of mathematics to another. In other words, a consistency proof by the method of models is only relative. Hilbert, therefore, conceived a new direct approach to the consistency problem. Much as one may prove, by the rules of a game, that certain situations cannot occur within the game, Hilbert hoped to prove, by a suitable set of rules of procedure for obtaining acceptable formulas from the basic symbols, that a contradictory formula can never occur. In logical notation, a contradictory formula is any formula of the type $F \wedge F'$, where F is some accepted formula of the system. If one can show that no such contradictory formula is possible, then one has established the consistency of the system.

The development of the above ideas of a direct test for consistency in mathematics is called, by Hilbert, the "proof theory." Hilbert and Bernays planned to give a detailed exposition (and application to all classical mathematics) of the proof theory in their great *Grundlagen der Mathematik*, which may be considered as the "Principia Mathematica" of the formalist school. The *Grundlagen der Mathematik* was finally published in two volumes, Volume I in 1934 and Volume II in 1939, but, as the work was being written, unforeseen difficulties arose, and it was not possible to complete the proof theory. For certain elementary systems, proofs of consistency were carried out, which illustrated what Hilbert would like to have done for all classical mathematics, but, for the system *in toto*, the problem of consistency remained refractory.

As a matter of fact, the Hilbert program, at least in the form originally envisioned by Hilbert, appears to be doomed to failure; this truth was brought out by Kurt Gödel in 1931, actually before the publication of the *Grundlagen* had taken place. Gödel showed, by unimpeachable methods acceptable to the followers of any one of the three principal schools of the philosophy of mathematics, that it is impossible for a sufficiently rich formalized deductive system, such as Hilbert's system for all classical mathematics, to prove consistency of the system by methods belonging to the system. This remarkable result is a consequence of an even more fundamental one; Gödel proved the incompleteness of Hilbert's system—that is, he established the existence within the system of "undecidable" problems, of which consistency of the system is one. These theorems of Gödel are too difficult to consider in their technical details here. They are certainly among the most remarkable in all mathematics, and they reveal an unforeseen limitation in the methods of formal mathematics. They show "that the formal systems known to be adequate for the derivation of mathematics are unsafe in the sense that their consistency cannot be demonstrated by finitary methods formalized within the system, whereas any system known to be safe in this sense is inadequate."[2]

NOTES

[1] Forewarnings of this crisis can be seen in the renowned paradoxes of Zeno of about 450 B.C.

[2] F. DE SUA. Here we also find the following interesting remark: "Suppose we loosely define a *religion* as any discipline whose foundations rest on an element of faith, irrespective of any element of reason which may be present. Quantum mechanics for example would be a religion under this definition. But mathematics would hold the unique position of being the only branch of theology possessing a rigorous demonstration of the fact that it should be so classified."

ON THE RELATION OF MATHEMATICS AND PHYSICS

ROBERT B. LINDSAY

Recent advances in nuclear physics dramatically emphasize the changes in methodology that have taken place from the time when, shortly before the turn of the century, Maxwell and Hertz ushered in a new era of science. Generally speaking, physical sciences are developed initially by the use of inductive procedures. A point is eventually reached, however, when these procedures alone no longer suffice, and the deductive processes of mathematics are then pressed into service.

We have already seen that modern mathematics is postulational in essence. Considered as a logico-deductive system, mathematics makes no pretense at interpreting the subject matter of its symbols. Thus a mathematical structure, of itself, possesses no meaning; nevertheless, it does have form, or a pattern. It is this pattern that serves the scientist so well. When the subject-matter symbols of a given mathematical structure-form have been appropriately particularized, the mathematics become a system in theoretical science, and the postulates of the mathematics become the laws of nature of science. The availability of many different mathematical structures has proved extremely fruitful.

On the Relation of Mathematics and Physics*

IT IS REPORTED that the greatest scientist who ever lived on this continent once remarked: "A mathematician may say anything he pleases, but a physicist must be at least partially sane." Most physicists and probably other scientists as well heartily agree with the first part of this dictum attributed to Willard Gibbs, but some of us are beginning to have our doubts about the second part. In these wartime days the word physicist is defined to mean a person who never gets a vacation, and few people bearing this title get even a moment or two to stop and think in the midst of their incessant preoccupation with the devising of bigger and better engines of destruction. And if we add to this group those who are busily engaged in instructing people how to use these engines of destruction, or teaching the fundamentals of physics to those who will ultimately have to use them (encountering in the process more than the normal "emotional resistance" to the subject), we may well wonder whether it is any longer fair to assume that physicists can remain even partially sane.

If this were a strictly logical presentation of the role of pure mathematics in physics, we should, of course, have to begin with *definitions*: "What is mathematics, what is physics, what is a relation, etc.?" There are numerous stunt definitions of these disciplines. From the eminent author of *Marriage and Morals* (and other somewhat more recondite works) we have long since learned that "pure mathematics is the class of all propositions of the form *'p* implies *q.'*" This means that mathematics is really symbolic logic, a subject already aptly described by another distinguished mathematician. Recall the famous dictum of Tweedledee in *Through the Looking Glass*. Said he to Alice in connection with some weighty mental matter: "Contrariwise, if it was so, it might be; and if it were so, it would be, but as it isn't, it ain't. That's logic." This remark about logic makes us the more ready to accept the even more notorious deliverance of the philosophical earl above quoted that "mathematics is the science in which we never know what we are talking about nor whether what we are saying is true." College students support this view whole-

* Reprinted from the *Scientific Monthly*, December 1944, vol. 59, pp. 456–460. By kind permission of the Science Press.

heartedly even when they do not understand its implications.

Just as familiar are the stunt definitions of physics, from the good old engineering version that "physics is the science of the ways of taking hold of things and pushing them" to the metaphysical cliché: "physics is only a state of mind." And speaking about metaphysics reminds us of the three-way comparison someone has made of philosophy, mathematics, and physics:

Philosophy has been a human activity for ages, and philosophers have long sought to understand the universe. As a result of their efforts they have at length come to know almost *nothing* about *everything*. On the other hand, the mathematicians, who have been equally eager to understand, have through the course of the centuries achieved the proud position where they know almost *everything* about *nothing*. Finally the mere physicist, a modest and humble soul, having tried very hard, has at last been able to learn a little *something* about *something*.

This sort of thing could be continued indefinitely, but this is enough for our purpose.

To the average physicist the fondness for generalization suggested in the parable just quoted is undoubtedly the chief characteristic of the pure mathematician. To be sure the physicist considers *he* is working mathematically when to the accompaniment of much perspiration and some profanity he evaluates a certain infinite integral (usually approximately!) or solves a certain recalcitrant differential equation (also usually approximately!). But the pure mathematician assures him that all this is not really mathematics—it is merely manipulating symbols and is probably wrong anyway, certainly so if it fails to come within the range of the appropriate existence theorems. For the pure mathematician is never interested in special cases unless they are strictly pathological. To him the proper aim of mathematical analysis is the establishment of the most general conclusion from the smallest number of restrictive hypotheses. Moreover, he refuses to permit any trace of uncertainty in the conclusions he draws; every element of his reasoning is scrutinized in the most severely critical manner, and anything that anyone else has to say about his reasoning is scrutinized with the same meticulous care. The results are open to the inspection of anyone who cares to examine a treatise on analysis. It will there be found that the pure mathematician would far rather say with absolute certainty something about continuous functions which are *not* differentiable than about functions which *are* differentiable. By the same token he feels even more pleasure in being able to say something about functions which are not even everywhere continuous.

This desire for maximum generality coupled with maximum rigor is very laudable. We certainly could stand a lot more application of the mathematician's ideal of rigorous, honest thinking in our daily lives and social relationships. Yet it cannot be denied that the emphasis on generality has, for the physicist, its inconvenient side. For it usually happens that the more general the theorem, the less it says which is useful to one interested in a specific application. Moreover, physicists are occasionally annoyed by the penchant of the mathematician for proving that under such and such conditions a solution of a certain equation exists without in the least indicating how to find it. But the latter is just the problem the physicist is worrying about. Actually he has little doubt about the existence of the solution: if the equation really represents a physical situation, there must be a solution.

But let us return to the question of the nature of mathematics, particularly in its relation to physics. It is appropriate to listen to what two distinguished physicists have said about it. In an address before the mathematical and physical section of the British Association at Liverpool in 1870, Clerk Maxwell made the following remarks:

> As mathematicians we perform certain mental operations on the symbols of number or of quantity and by proceeding step by step from more simple to more complex operations, we are enabled to express the same thing in many different forms. The equivalence of these different forms, though a necessary consequence of self-evident axioms, is not always to our minds self-evident, but the mathematician who by long practice has acquired a familiarity with many of these forms and has become expert in the processes which lead from one to another, can often transform a perplexing expression into another which explains its meaning in more intelligible language.

Maxwell then went on to state succinctly what we do as *physicists* in an attempted description of natural phenomena.

In elaborating on the relation between the two forms of activity he finally comes to the part which appears particularly apropos of our present discussion. I quote again:

There are men who, when any relation or law, however complex, is put before them in a symbolical form, can grasp its full meaning as a relation among abstract quantities. Such men sometimes treat with indifference the further statement that quantities actually exist in nature which fulfil this relation. The mental image of the concrete reality seems rather to disturb than to assist their contemplations.

But the great majority of mankind are utterly unable, without long training, to retain in their minds the unembodied symbols of the pure mathematician, so that, if science is ever to become popular, and yet remain scientific, it must be by a profound study and a copious application of the mathematical classification of quantities which lies at the root of every truly scientific illustration.

There are, as I have said, some minds which can go on contemplating with satisfaction pure quantities presented to the eye by symbols, and to the mind in a form which none but mathematicians can conceive.

There are others who feel more enjoyment in following geometrical forms, which they draw on paper, or build in the empty space before them.

Others again, are not content unless they can project their whole physical energies into the scene which they conjure up. They learn at what rate the planets rush through space, and they experience a delightful feeling of exhilaration. They calculate the forces with which the heavenly bodies pull at one another, and they feel their own muscles straining with the effort.

To such men momentum, energy, mass are not mere abstract expressions of the results of scientific inquiry. They are words of power, which stir their souls like the memories of childhood.

For the sake of persons of different types, scientific truth should be presented in different forms, and should be regarded as equally scientific, whether it appears in the robust form and the vivid colouring of a physical illustration, or in the tenuity and paleness of a symbolical expression.

So much for Maxwell! We are now ready for the opinion of the other physicist referred to above. The story goes that at a Yale faculty meeting at which the discussion grew long-winded (as it is apt to do on such occasions) on the comparative merits of courses in English, mathematics, modern languages, etc., the usually silent professor of mathematical physics finally rose and said with decided emphasis: "Mathematics *is* a language."

I have often wondered whether this is the basis on which students of mathematics in liberal arts colleges secure election to Phi Beta Kappa! I doubt whether Gibbs had this in mind, if he actually made this statement, which after all is merely an abbreviated form of Maxwell's comments. Mathematics *is* the language of physical science and certainly no more marvelous language was ever created by the mind of man.

In view of this it would certainly strike an ignorant bystander as paradoxical, or at least somewhat surprising, that the general public and indeed many physicists view with a mixture of suspicion and repugnance the increasing use of mathematics in physics. It is well known how difficult it is to make college students really use in elementary and intermediate college physics the mathematics they have learned in mathematics courses. A few years ago I thought it was possible to detect a trend toward the closer co-operation between elementary mathematics and physics, which would permit the early use of the calculus in physics teaching. This is not so clear today. The war situation should discourage hasty generalization, but I think we must reckon on the odd repugnance of the generality of mankind to deal with an abstract symbolism. This is a psychological problem of great interest though of great difficulty and one not within my competence. I am told by certain authorities that many persons are constitutionally unable to think mathematically, i.e., in terms of abstract symbols. This has always struck me as curious, for it seems to me that all persons who think logically at all are effectively thinking mathematically whether they are willing to admit it or not. The learning of a special symbolism is a mere device to facilitate logical thinking, and unwillingness to learn it probably reflects human inertia more than human incompetence. The equation of continuity of an incompressible fluid in the form $\nabla \cdot (\rho v) = 0$ may leave the average citizen cold but he ought to be made to realize that he actually understands what it means if only he grasps the significance of that famous bar room which, I understand, exists in the city of San Francisco: it has two doors and whenever anyone enters one door, someone *has* to leave by the other. It is not at all a difficult concept to get hold of, viewed thus pictorially. Like the hero in Molière's play, who was astonished to find out that he had been talking prose all his life, many of our contemporaries would doubtless be amazed to learn of the amount of mathematics they really know!

Mathematics is a language marvelously adapted to the description of natural phenomena, but we must be careful to impress on everyone the necessity for understanding what the language says. Too many persons think of theoretical physics, for example, as mere juggling with symbols and symbolic relations. But the mathematical manipulation is meaningless without an understanding of the physical content. No matter how abstract a concept is, even if it is a quantum mechanical Ψ function, a definite physical significance should be attached to the concept, which follows it wherever it wanders throughout the mathematical analysis. If we were more careful to follow this recipe we might prevent theoretical physics from becoming a mere meaningless algorithm for the prediction of the results of experiments. In this connection I like to recall what Maxwell had to say about Faraday in the preface to the first edition of the celebrated *Treatise on Electricity and Magnetism*. It will be remembered that he began the composition of his work with the supposition, common at that time, that there was a decided difference between Faraday's way of looking at electrical phenomena and that of the continental school of mathematicians. However, as he proceeded with his study of the *Experimental Researches in Electricity*, he became convinced that Faraday's method of description was also a mathematical one, even if not expressed in the conventional mathematical symbolism of the time. Actually we now recognize that Faraday originated the field concept in electrical science and that Maxwell's great contribution was in translating Faraday's theory into the accepted mathematical notation of the nineteenth century. But the point for us to note is that in the use of his geometry of lines of force, Faraday reasoned mathematically in very decisive fashion. It is not at all unlikely that the more powerful modes of nonmetrical mathematical thinking typified by modern topology may ultimately find as useful an application to modern physics as Faraday's original geometrical notions.

We are all familiar with the fondness physicists display for analogies. They are used freely in teaching and in certain fields they have proved a powerful research tool. Think in this connection of the utility of electromechanical analogies in the field of communications. Their outstanding success has led to a peculiar situation: in order to explain to an electrical engineer, for example, how a mechanical filter works, it is necessary to replace the actual collection of masses and couplings by an equivalent set of inductances, capacitances, and resistances. Only then does he really understand it! Now the point about this which is relevant for our present purpose is that the successful use of the method of analogy depends solely on the mathematical equivalence of the schemes used to describe the phenomena in question. It takes little thought to see that such analogies never could have been developed from physical intuition based on observation alone. Certainly a cylindrical tube with alternate constrictions and expansions in its cross section bears no remote resemblance in its physical appearance to an iterated combination of coils of wire and condensers. It is only when we examine the two structures mathematically that we recognize that the tube behaves ideally with respect to acoustic wave transmission the same as the inductance-condenser structure with respect to electric wave transmission. Certainly there is a tremendous gain in the efficiency of our thinking in our recognition that both structures can be considered as energy-transmitting systems which are selective with respect to frequency.

The above illustration suggests the important role played in the progress of physical methodology by the choice of an appropriate notation which can be applied successfully to a wide diversity of phenomena. An example closely allied to what we have been discussing is found in the impedance notation for the ratio of a pressure analogue to a flow analogue. It is scarcely an exaggeration to say that this notion alone has opened the book of acoustics to electrical engineers who would have turned pale at the very mention of the name of Lord Rayleigh. It seems only fair to admit that it did not take the impedance notation to make the theory of acoustics clear to Lord Rayleigh; however, it certainly has made the use of acoustics much easier to hundreds of persons, and this is justification enough.

There is a converse to the picture. The mind of man is a strange thing; not content to economize by using the same mathematical notation to describe the most diverse phenomena, it feels that it gains a deeper insight into one particular section of experience by describing it with a wide variety of mathematical methods. A mathematics professor of mine many years ago used to say that it is much more illuminating to solve one problem by two or more different methods than any number of problems by the same method. It is hard to convince beginning college students of the validity of this point of view; they have apparently been too carefully conditioned against it by their secondary school education. But I think we must all admit that this is an idea which has led to tremendous strides in physics as well as in mathematics. Everyone knows that it is perfectly possible to develop the theory of elastic media in terms of sets of simultaneous equations connecting stress components with strain components. But think how much more insight is gained in these problems if we translate the results into tensor analysis notation! Maxwell stressed this point of view in his remark that "mathematics is the art of saying the same thing in many different ways." We must not be too much disturbed if the language tends to grow more abstract as this process evolves.

The reference to the word "art" in Maxwell's remark serves to remind us that much attention has been paid to this aspect of mathematics as something created by the mind of man, possessing no necessary connection with his external environment and being in this sense akin to all other artistic creations, transcending common experience and common sense. What relation, if any, does this view have to physics? Certainly the study of history shows that early mathematics developed from the desire to describe nature more precisely than in terms of common language. Nearly all the early celebrated mathematicians were also natural philosophers. However, in more recent times, mathematicians have preferred to construct their abstractions without reference to the physical world and work with entities "that never were on land or sea." Physicists are apt to grow impatient with this sort of thing and label it mysticism or worse. It might be fairer if we compared it with music or art as an expression of man's emotions. G. H. Hardy in his recent book, *A Mathematician's Apology*, expresses openly the conviction that what he calls "real" mathematics must be justified as art if it can be justified at all—it has no other defense. Like poetry or music it promotes and sustains a lofty habit of mind. For one of the most enthusiastic panegyrics on mathematics from this standpoint I can recommend nothing better than the introduction to Lord Brougham's biographical sketch of d'Alembert. Brougham was an amateur mathematician along with his other versatile traits. Physicists may not like his treatment of Thomas Young and certainly he was pretty far wrong in his estimate of the wave theory of light, but we cannot help being impressed by the sonorous Victorian prose in which he emphasizes the depth of the pure mathematician's immersion in his subject, his attention abstracted from all lesser considerations, and his mind reflecting a calm and agreeable temper. The sublime effect is a bit weakened indeed when he solemnly asserts that "instances are well known of a habit of drinking being cured by the intensity of attention to mathematical researches." Moreover, we learn also that "an inveterate taste for gambling has been found to give way before the revival of an early love of analytical studies!"

On the whole, physicists should be glad that pure mathematicians exist and in fact ought to be willing to subsidize them if their limited means allowed. For it is becoming more and more clear that the pure mathematics of today will be the physics of tomorrow. This does not mean that the fertilization of mathematics by physics is over. On the contrary, the creation of new mathematical methods for the solution of physical problems proceeds at an accelerated pace. The vast amount of interest in operational methods initiated by Heaviside's operational calculus and the even newer work on nonlinear systems provide good illustrations. This is the field of mathematical physics—a genuine branch of mathematics, too often confused in popular parlance with theoretical physics, which is physics and not mathematics. If I may insert a parenthetical remark, it would be better not to use the terms mathematical physicist and theoretical physicist as synonyms—it is not wholly a trivial matter when it comes to placing people in jobs where they can do the most good.

It is becoming more keenly realized that mathematical physics is a more difficult field of endeavor than pure mathematics. For the pure mathematician creates his own problems, and if he strikes one he cannot solve, he usually manages to find another somewhat like it which he can solve. But the mathematical physicist has to take the problems which nature provides—he cannot dodge them. For this reason it is very important for the progress of physics that as many as possible of the best mathematical minds of the world shall devote their attention to mathematical physics. Under the impact of war this is taking place to a greater extent than ever before in this country. We may well hope that the progress suffers no check!

As long as man retains his curiosity about his environment, he will try to describe nature, and as long as he expresses his interpretation in terms of relations among apparently diverse phenomena, he will continue to use mathematical reasoning; this will remain true whether we are concerned with metrical or nonmetrical aspects of experience. Of one thing we may be sure: physics without mathematics will forever be incomprehensible.

MATHEMATICS: METHOD AND ART

Morris Kline

Most of us are aware of the role played by mathematics in the market place and as handmaiden to the arts and sciences. Perhaps less widely appreciated is the role of mathematics as a guide to pure thought, intimately associated with logic and philosophy.

In the present essay, Professor Kline clearly reveals the distinction between pure mathematics and applied mathematics. He explains the abstract nature of mathematical systems and their relation to physical meanings. The mathematician is completely free to deal with undefined terms; later, when these undefined terms are given various unrelated interpretations, the results may nevertheless prove highly significant and useful. Thus, precisely because the things that the axioms talk about are meaningless to begin with, the system built upon those axioms becomes a powerful tool of thought.

Mathematics: Method and Art*

. . . MATHEMATICS is, itself, a living, flourishing branch of our culture. Several thousand years of development have produced an imposing body of thought whose essential characteristics should be familiar to every educated person. Though the nature of modern mathematics was somewhat foreshadowed by the contributions of the Greeks, the events of the intervening centuries and the creation of non-Euclidean geometry in particular have radically altered the role and character of the subject. An examination of the nature of twentieth-century mathematics will not only redress a wrong but will perhaps make it evident why the subject has gained in power and stature.

More than anything else mathematics is a method. The method is embodied in each of the branches of mathematics, such as the algebra of real numbers, Euclidean geometry, or any non-Euclidean geometry. By examining the common structure of these branches, the salient features of this method will become clear.

Any one branch or system of mathematics deals with a class of concepts pertinent to it; for example, Euclidean geometry deals with points, lines, triangles, circles, and so on. Precise definitions of the concepts belonging to a system are all-important foundation stones on which the delicate superstructure is built. Unfortunately not every concept or term can be defined without entering upon an unending succession of definitions. It is true that the meanings of the undefined terms are suggested by physical examples. Addition, one of the undefined terms of algebra, can be explained by talking in terms of the number of cows that would be obtained by forming one herd from two separate herds. But such explanations in physical terms are not part of mathematics, for the subject is logically independent and self-sufficient. Of course, some concepts can be defined by appealing to the undefined ones, just as *circle* can be defined in

* Reprinted from Morris Kline, *Mathematics in Western Culture*, 1953, pp. 453–466. By permission and courtesy of the Oxford University Press and George Allen & Unwin, Ltd., London.

terms of point, plane, and distance by describing it as the set of all points in a plane at a fixed distance from a given point.

If some terms are undefined and the physical pictures and processes we customarily associate with these terms are not part of mathematics proper, what facts about them can we use in the reasoning? The answer is to be found in the axioms. These assertions about the undefined and defined terms, which we accept without proof, are the sole basis for any conclusions that may be drawn about the concepts under discussion.

But how do we know what axioms to accept, especially in view of the fact that they involve undefined terms? Are we not in the position of dogs chasing their own tails? As in the case of the undefined terms, experience usually supplies the answer. Men accepted the axioms about number and the axioms of Euclidean geometry because experience with collections of objects and with physical figures vouched for these axioms. Here, too, we must caution against including the physical experience as part of mathematics. Mathematics begins with the statement of the axioms regardless of where they are obtained. Experience was the sole source of axioms until the nineteenth century. The investigations in non-Euclidean geometry, however, were motivated by a desire to use a parallel axiom different from Euclid's. In these cases mathematicians were deliberately going contrary to experience.

Though the axioms of non-Euclidean geometry appeared to be contrary to ordinary human experience they yielded theorems applicable to the physical world. In view of this fact it would seem that there should be considerable latitude in the choice of axioms. This is a partial truth, for the axioms of *any one* branch of mathematics must be consistent with each other, or else only confusion results. Consistency means not only that the axioms must not contradict each other but that they must not give rise to theorems which contradict each other.

The requirement of consistency has begun to take on great significance in recent years. As long as mathematicians regarded their axioms and theorems as absolute truths, it did not occur to them that contradictions could ever arise, except through an error in logic. Nature was consistent. Since mathematics phrased facts of nature in its axioms and deduced other truths not immediately apprehended in nature, mathematics also had to be consistent. The creation of non-Euclidean geometry, however, caused the mathematicians to see that they must stand on their own feet. They were not recording nature; they were interpreting. And any interpretation might not only be wrong but might also be inconsistent. The problem of consistency was further emphasized by the discovery of paradoxes involving fundamental concepts, a discovery that followed in the train of Cantor's contributions.

It may be possible to determine by direct examination of a set of axioms that no one of them contradicts another. But how can we be sure that not one of the hundreds of theorems which may be deducible from the axioms will ever contradict another? The answer to this question is lengthy and, it must be confessed, not entirely satisfactory at the present time. Much recent work in mathematics has been directed toward establishing the consistency of the many mathematical branches. Mathematicians, however, have been balked, at least thus far, in their efforts to prove that the mathematical system which comprises the axioms and theorems about our ordinary real number system is consistent. The situation is extremely embarrassing. In recent years consistency replaced truth as the god of mathematicians and now there is a likelihood that this god too may not exist.

In addition to being consistent with each other, the axioms of a branch of mathematics should be simple. The reason for this requirement is clear. Inasmuch as axioms are accepted without proof, we should be aware of precisely what we are agreeing to. Simplicity insures this understanding. It is preferable, though not essential, that the axioms of a mathematical system be independent of each other. That is, it should not be possible to *deduce* an axiom from one or more of the others. The axiom that can be so deduced is better affirmed as a theorem, for we thereby reduce to as small a number as possible the statements accepted without proof. Finally, the axioms of a mathematical system must be fruitful; like carefully selected seeds they must yield a valuable crop, for one objective of mathematical activity is to obtain the new knowledge and insight implicit in the axioms. Euclid's contribution to mathematics was valuable because he chose a simple set of axioms that yielded hundreds of theorems.

Granted that a set of axioms fulfilling all the necessary and desirable conditions has been selected, how does the mathematician know what theorems to prove and how does he go about proving them? Let us consider these questions in turn.

There are many sources of possible theorems. Of such sources experience is by far the most fruitful. Experience with physical or real triangles suggests many likely conclusions about mathematical triangles. Deduction from the axioms then either establishes these conclusions as theorems of mathematics or discredits them. Of course experience must be understood in a broad sense. Random observations sometimes suggest possible theorems. Scientific problems arising in laboratories or observatories and the artistic problem of depicting depth on a flat surface have led to precise theorems.

To a large extent mathematics generates its own problems. Many a possible theorem arises as a generalization of observations about numbers and geometrical figures. Anyone who has played with integers, for example, has doubtless observed that the sum of the first *two* odd numbers, that is, $1 + 3$, is the square of *two;* the sum of the first *three* odd numbers, that is, $1 + 3 + 5$, is the square of *three;* and similarly for the first four, five, and six odd numbers. Thus simple calculation suggests a general statement, namely, that the sum of the first n odd numbers, where n is any positive integer, is the square of n. Of course this possible theorem is not proved by the calculations above. Nor could it ever be proved by such calculations, for no mortal man could make the infinite set of calculations that would be required to establish the conclusion for *every* n. The calculations do, however, give the mathematician something to work on.

Consider another instance of generalization as a source of suggestions for theorems. A triangle is a polygon of three sides. Now in Euclidean geometry the sum of the angles of a triangle is $180°$. Is it not natural to ask whether any general theorem could be found about the sum of the angles of any polygon? This question is answered by a very old theorem. The sum of the angles of any polygon is found by subtracting two from the number of sides and then multiplying the result by $180°$.

We have already seen how the purely logical problem of

deducing the assertion contained in Euclid's parallel axiom from more acceptable axioms led to non-Euclidean geometry. Once the idea of such geometries was grasped numerous suggestions for theorems were obtained by seeking the analogues of theorems that held in Euclidean geometry. For example, what is the analogue of the theorem that the sum of the angles of a quadrilateral is 360°?

These few indications of how the mathematician secures suggestions for theorems do not tell the whole story. Even if we add the more fortuitous sources such as pure chance, guesswork, and blundering about until a theorem is found, we still have left out the most valuable source of possible theorems—the imagination, intuition, and insight of creative genius. Most people could look at a quadrilateral indefinitely without becoming aware that if the midpoints of the four sides are joined, the figure formed is a parallelogram. Such knowledge is not the product of logic but of a sudden flash of insight.

In the domains of algebra, calculus, and advanced analysis especially, the first-rate mathematician depends on the kind of inspiration that we usually associate with the composer of music. The composer feels that he has a theme, a phrase which, when properly developed and embroidered, will produce beautiful music. Experience and a knowledge of music

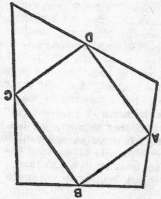

The lines joining the midpoints of the sides of any quadrilateral form a parallelogram.

aid him in developing it. Similarly the mathematician divines that he has a conclusion which will follow from the axioms. Experience and knowledge may guide his thoughts into the proper channels. Modifications of one sort or another may be required before a correct and satisfactory statement of the new theorem is achieved. But essentially both mathematician and composer are moved by a divine afflatus that enables them to "see" and "know" the final edifice before one stone is laid.

Knowing *what* to prove is inextricably involved with knowing *how* to prove it. The mathematician may be convinced from an examination of the known facts in a situation that it should be possible to prove a certain theorem. But until he can give a deductive proof of this theorem he cannot assert or apply it. The distinction between conviction that a theorem should hold and proof of the theorem is made clear by many classic examples. The Greeks proposed the three famous problems of doubling a cube, trisecting an angle, and squaring a circle by means of a straightedge and compass. Over a period of two thousand years many a mathematician was convinced that it was impossible to perform these constructions under the conditions stated, but it was not until definite proofs of the impossibility were given in the nineteenth century that the problems were considered settled.

An excellent example of a conjecture, the truth of which seems indubitable, is that every even number is the sum of two prime numbers. A prime number, let it be remembered, is a whole number divisible only by itself and 1; thus 13 is a prime number but 9 is not. In accordance with this conjecture 2 is $1 + 1$; 4 is $2 + 2$; 6 is $3 + 3$; 8 is $3 + 5$; 10 is $3 + 7$; and so on. We could continue to test even numbers indefinitely and we should find that the conjecture holds. This conjecture is not a theorem of mathematics, however, because no proof of it has thus far been given.

A theorem must be established beyond question by deductive reasoning from axioms, and mathematicians literally work thousands of years to obtain such proofs. In our daily use of the phrases "mathematical exactness" and "mathematical precision" we pay homage to this unrelenting search for certainty.

Evidently much mathematical work must be done to find methods of proof even after the question of what to prove is disposed of. This point needs no emphasis for those readers who have struggled with exercises in geometry wherein the statement of what to prove is given and the student is expected to take over from that point. In the search for a method of proof, as in finding what to prove, the mathematician must use imagination, insight, and creative ability. He must see possible lines of attack where others would not, and he must have the mental stamina to wrestle with a problem until he has succeeded in finding a solution. Just what goes on in his mind while he works on the problem we do not know, any more than we know exactly what thought processes inspired Keats to write fine poetry or why Rembrandt's hands and brain were able to turn out paintings that suggest great psychological depth. We cannot define genius. We can only say that creative ability in mathematics calls for mental qualities of unusual excellence.

Perhaps we have been riding our Pegasus too hard and too high. Having anticipated a theorem and having then established it, has the mathematician really learned something new? After all, he derives from the axioms only what he puts into them, since all the conclusions that follow are logically implicit in the axioms. Mathematicians adopt axioms and spend centuries deducing theorems that are actually no more than elaborations of what the axioms say. In the words of the philosopher, Wittgenstein, mathematics is just a grand tautology.

But how grand! It is literally correct to describe the logical structure of mathematics as a tautology, but this statement is about as adequate as saying that Venus de Milo is just a big girl. The description of mathematics as a tautology says that the choice of a set of axioms is like the purchase of a piece of mining land—the riches are all there. This description omits, however, the patient, hard digging which must be performed, the careful sifting of the precious metal from the base rock, the value and beauty of the treasure obtained, and the pleasure and exhilaration of accomplishment.

The divination and establishment of theorems complete the structure of a branch of mathematics. Such a branch, then, comprises terms, undefined and defined, axioms, and theorems proved on the basis of these axioms. This analysis of a mathematical system describes the structure of the mathematics of number and the structure of each of the geometries. It thus seems to epitomize the nature of mathematics. But a fuller appreciation of our subject calls for a little deeper investigation.

Every mathematical system contains undefined terms: for example, the words *point* and *line* in a geometrical system. In our discussion of the non-Euclidean geometries we found that we can attach physical meanings to the word *line* that differ considerably from the stretched string mathematicians had in mind in constructing these geometries. The fact that we can take such liberties with undefined terms, that we can give them seemingly unwarranted interpretations, suggests some deeper significance in the existence of undefined terms than has heretofore been made evident. . . .

A fact of great consequence should now be clear: *In deductive proof from explicitly stated axioms the meaning of the undefined terms is irrelevant.* The mathematician of today realizes that any physical meaning can be attached to point, line, and other undefined terms as long as the axioms involving these terms hold for the physical meanings. If the axioms do hold, then the theorems also apply to these physical interpretations.

It would seem that our new conception of the nature of mathematics robs it of all its meaning. Instead of being inseparably related to definite physical concepts and giving us insights into the physical world, it now appears to be concerned with empty words "signifying nothing." But the reverse is true. Mathematics is far richer in meaning, vaster in scope, and more fruitful in application than had ever been suspected before. In addition to the physical meanings which were formerly associated with mathematical concepts and can still be retained, an unlimited variety of new meanings may be found that satisfy the axioms of mathematical systems. In such new situations the theorems of these systems have new meanings and hence new applications.

Yet pure mathematics itself is not immediately or primarily concerned with the special meanings that may be given to the undefined terms. Rather it is concerned with the deductions that can be made from the axioms and the defined concepts. Applied mathematics, on the other hand, is concerned with those physical meanings of the concepts of pure mathematics that render the theorems useful in scientific work. The transition from pure to applied mathematics usually goes unnoticed. The statment that the area of a circle is πr^2 is a theorem of pure mathematics. The statement that the area of a circular field is π times the square of a certain physical length is a theorem of applied mathematics.

The distinction we have drawn between pure and applied mathematics is precisely what Bertrand Russell had in mind when he made the seemingly flippant but entirely justified remark that pure "mathematics is the subject in which we never know what we are talking about, nor whether what we are saying is true." Of course many a person has entertained such thoughts about mathematics without encouragement from Russell. He may not have known, however, how true they were or how to justify them. Mathematicians do not know what they are talking about because pure mathematics is not concerned with physical meaning. Mathematicians never know whether what they are saying is true because, as pure mathematicians, they make no effort to ascertain whether their theorems are true assertions about the physical world. Of such theorems we may ask only whether they were obtained by correct reasoning. . . .

The abstractness of mathematical thinking results from the fact that mathematics proper drops the physical meanings originally associated with the undefined terms. Mathematical method is abstract in another sense as well. Out of the medley of experiences proffered by nature, mathematics isolates and concentrates on particular aspects. This is abstraction in the sense of delimiting the phenomenon under investigation. For example, the mathematical straight line has only a few properties compared to those of the straight lines made by the edge of a table or drawn with pencil. The few properties the mathematical line possesses are stated in the axioms; for example, it is determined by two points. The physical lines, in addition to this property, have color and even breadth and depth; moreover, they are built up of molecules each of which has a complicated structure.

It would seem offhand that an attempt to study nature by concentrating on just a few properties of physical objects would fall far short of effectiveness. Yet part of the secret of mathematical power lies in the use of this type of abstraction. By this means we free our minds from burdensome and irrelevant detail and are thereby able to accomplish more than if we had to keep the whole physical picture before us.

The success of the process of abstracting particular aspects of nature rests on the divide-and-conquer rule.

In addition to delimiting the problem being studied there are further advantages in concentrating on a few aspects of experience. The experimental scientist, because he deals so directly with physical objects, is usually limited to thinking in terms of objects perceived through the senses. He is chained to the ground. Mathematics, by abstracting concepts and properties from the physical objects, is able to fly on wings of thought beyond the sensible world of sight, sound, and touch. Thus mathematics can "handle" such "things" as bundles of energy, which perhaps can never be qualitatively described because they are apparently beyond the realm of sensation. Mathematics can "explain" gravitation, for example, as a property of a space too vast to visualize. In like manner mathematics can treat and "know" such mysterious phenomena as electricity, radio waves, and light for which any physical picture is mainly speculative and always inadequate. The abstractions, that is the mathematical formulas, are the most significant and the most useful facts we have about these phenomena.

Abstracting quantitative aspects of physical phenomena often reveals unsuspected relationships because the quantitative laws turn out to be the same for apparently unrelated phenomena. This statement is nowhere better illustrated than by Maxwell's discovery that electromagnetic waves and light waves satisfy the same differential equations. It suggested at once that light and electromagnetic waves possess the same physical properties, a relationship confirmed a thousand times since. As Whitehead says:

> Nothing is more impressive than the fact that as mathematics withdrew increasingly into the upper regions of ever greater extremes of abstract thought, it returned back to earth with a corresponding growth of importance for the analysis of concrete fact. . . . The paradox is now fully established that the utmost abstractions are the true weapons with which to control our thought of concrete fact.

Those who, admitting the paradox, still deplore the fact that to achieve success the physical sciences have to pay the price of mathematical abstractness must reconsider what it is they would look for in a scientific exposition of the nature of the physical world. Eddington's answer is that a knowledge of mathematical relations and structure is all that the science of physics can give us. And Jeans says that the mathematical description of the universe *is* the ultimate reality.

MATHEMATICS AND MASTERPIECES, OR A NEW DIMENSION OF CULTURE

ELMER C. EASTON

For some reason not too well understood, mathematics is admirably suited for describing physical phenomena. Preliminary mathematical computations are commonly used when designing machines and engineering structures according to desired specifications.

Far more dramatic, however, is the role played by mathematics in predicting possible properties or behavior of a physical system even before it has been created, notably in the field of electrical engineering. In the present essay, Dr. Easton explains in a remarkably simple way how the mathematician, by using very advanced mathematics, was able to predict the possibility of fabricating a physical material which offers both positive and negative electrical resistance. Such sophisticated use of abstract mathematics is highly significant and surely deserves the epithet "a new dimension of culture."

Dr. Easton is Dean of the College of Engineering, Rutgers University.

Mathematics and Masterpieces, or A New Dimension of Culture*

ONE OF THE CHARACTERISTICS which distinguish man from the lower animals is his ability to create and admire beautiful objects and beautiful ideas. Many of the lower animals create simple objects such as nests or burrows, but this activity is instinctive and the objects are monotonously similar. There is no evidence to indicate that these animals recognize differences of quality in the construction. Certainly, the lower animals do not gather to admire an especially well-built nest. It is quite certain that these animals do not produce ideas which are then discussed and admired by others of their group. Most of animal behavior is related directly to activities needed to sustain life.

Man, on the other hand, has always engaged in some sort of activity not directly needed for the sustaining of life. For example, some of the earliest known implements used by man show evidence of decoration. The decoration was obviously intended to enhance the beauty rather than the utility of the implements. Some of the very early cave dwellings reveal illustrations of animals drawn on the walls. From his very primitive beginnings man has always devoted some of his time to non-utilitarian pursuits designed solely to beautify his surroundings.

Archeological exploration has shown that very early in human history men recognized and valued good design and good workmanship. Unusually beautiful objects such as bowls, images and drawings were carefully preserved in safe places. Interesting ideas were also preserved as is shown by widespread imitation of certain patterns of design or styles of drawing.

The sounds which men made with their voices undoubtedly were used originally as signals, to frighten an enemy, to warn a child of danger or to express amorous intentions toward a

* Reprinted from *The New Jersey Mathematics Teacher*, October, 1961. By permission of Dean Elmer C. Easton, of the College of Engineering, Rutgers, The State University, and by courtesy of the Association of Mathematics Teachers of New Jersey.

mate. Slowly the intelligence of man began to organize the shouts, cries and grunts into meaningful patterns that could be recognized as having fixed meanings. As this primitive language developed, man must have become more and more intrigued by the sounds that he could make. He imitated other animals and used these imitations to attract his prey. It is likely that most of the early vocal efforts had purposes which were either ultilitarian or imitative. However, somewhere in his evolution man discovered that certain combinations and sequences of sounds could evoke emotional responses without having any relation to words, animal calls or recognizable noises. Some arrangements of sounds could make people smile, other arrangements could cause apprehension, some produced languorous moods. The ability of a man to combine sounds so as to evoke emotions became recognized as a skill to be admired and cultivated. Many people have attempted to compose what we now call music but relatively few have succeeded in producing the desired effect. Clearly it is not enough simply to make noises. To create music the noises must be organized in subtle ways so as to excite the emotions. The separate sounds must merge to form a unified sequence which, acting as a unit, can call forth an emotional response.

Similar efforts to stimulate the emotions through visual symbols are made by painters and sculptors, especially those of the abstractionist school. Some paintings and sculptures are directly representational. They imitate a subject as the human voice might imitate a bird call. On the other hand non-representational work might not resemble anything ever seen by man, yet, like music that does not imitate nature, it may arouse an emotional response in the viewer. The response is due to the effect of the work as a whole and not to the individual bits of paint or stone which form it. The success of the artist or sculptor is measured in terms of his ability to create a composition of color and form which, acting as a unified whole, causes the viewer to experience an emotional response.

Words themselves may be used for representational or abstract purposes. A writer may use words to describe an event so specifically that his reader may form a clear mental picture of it. On the other hand a poet may use words simply to form interesting patterns of rhythm, sound and symbolism which merge in the reader's mind to arouse an emotional reaction. A literal translation of the words of a poem may be almost meaningless in terms of representation, yet the reading of the words as they are combined in the poem may create a sensation which the reader finds interesting.

It must be noted that the effect of words, sounds, color and form exists only in the mind of some person. The effect on that mind depends on the extent to which the various individual elements of the stimulus are integrated to form a unified whole. It is the combination of elements working as a unit which produces the mental sensation. People who are the most skilful in combining diverse elements into unity are called masters, and their best works are called masterpieces.

The masters deserve great credit for their ability, yet their work would be largely futile if it were not for people who could recognize and respond to their masterpieces. If the Mona Lisa were hung where it could be seen only by dogs and cats it would be worthless. It is valued as a masterpiece because it is seen by people who recognize its quality and who react emotionally to its presence.

The more sophisticated a masterpiece is, the more its value depends on the understanding of the viewer. Beauty consists of the skilful combining of diverse elements into unity. In order to appreciate beauty the viewer must recognize the diverse elements and admire the skill with which they are combined to form a unified image.

When speaking of art forms it is often said that people do not know what they like, they like what they know. It often takes many years for a work to be recognized as a masterpiece. It takes a long time for people to learn enough about the work to recognize the genius of its creator. Frequently the master will employ concepts not understood by his contemporary public. The value of his work remains obscured until the people have learned to appreciate those concepts.

Thousands of years ago the human race developed the primitive art forms of painting, sculpture, poetry and music. The simplest examples of these forms can be appreciated by people in the earliest stages of cultural development. Although these classical media of expression have been refined over the years, no essentially new art forms were developed until the nineteenth century when scientific principles were used as the basis for the design of man's tools. The new form has entered a sophisticated stage in the middle of the twentieth century. It now represents a new dimension of culture.

Prior to the nineteenth century the tools which man used to extend his control over the forces and materials of nature were designed almost intuitively. When improvements were made they were largely the result of trial and error. Very little was known about the physical principles which governed the behavior of those tools, and even when some of the principles were known there were such gaps in the knowledge of the behavior of related elements that the principles could not be effectively employed. For example, the principle of the lever was described in mathematical terms many centuries ago. However, the maximum use could not be made of that formulation in early times because there was no mathematical technique of predicting the behavior of the material of which the lever and fulcrum might be constructed. Certainly there was no way to design new materials to meet extraordinary conditions.

In the fifteenth century Leonardo da Vinci epitomized the great ferment of scientific activity which was beginning to take place. His notebooks with their familiar sketches of actual and proposed devices illustrate the great range of interest in the fields of mathematics, mechanics, physics and astronomy possessed by the early generation of that century. The almost feverish desire to study the principles of these sciences was marked more by a breadth of investigation than by a depth of understanding.

During the sixteenth century conflicts arose among the scientists and the churchmen leading to such incidents as the trial of Galileo and the burning at the stake of Giordano Bruno in 1600. Nevertheless the thrill of discovering the laws of nature spurred men to overcome prejudice and superstition and led rapidly to the organization of societies dedicated to the strengthening of scientific knowledge.

The Royal Society was organized in England in 1662. The French Académie des Sciences was formed in 1666, and the Berlin Academy of Sciences in 1700. These learned groups provided a means for the rapid exchange of information among scientific investigators and made it possible quickly to identify areas in which vital basic information was lacking. The result was a rapid expansion of knowledge of physical principles and a deeper understanding of the laws which govern the behavior of the universe.

In most cases the empirical development of the earliest machines preceded and led to the discovery of the physical laws which governed their behavior. The machines used levers, wheels, cranks and gears which a man could hold in his hand. He could draw pictures of these parts and could visualize the way one might react on another even though he could not predict the magnitude of the reaction mathematically.

In the sixteenth century men were building a variety of crude machines which were operated by levers, gears, screws and pistons. Many ingenious pumps had been built to pump out mines, furnish drinking water and operate fire engines. Perhaps the earliest steam engine was a steam operated pump designed by the Marquess of Worcester in 1663. Soon after, Denis Papin of France devised a variation of the Worcester engine in a fashion such that it could turn a shaft. Using this engine Papin built a steamboat in 1707; however the local guild of boatmen destroyed the vessel before it could be operated. In the meantime, Newcomen and Calley in England had built successful steam engines in 1705.

The inventors of these early steam engines had no knowledge of the physical laws which governed their behavior. The design was wholly empirical. Hot steam pushed a piston in a cylinder. The cylinder was then flushed of steam by cold water, and atmospheric pressure on the opposite side caused the piston to return to its starting point. Enormous amounts of steam were wasted in heating the cylinder rather than in doing useful work.

The first major improvement in the steam engine was made by the Scottish engineer James Watt in 1765. By this date the nature of heat was beginning to be known both qualitatively and quantitatively. Using the new knowledge, Watt kept the cylinder hot and used a "condenser" to reduce the pressure of the steam after it had pushed the piston. Watt's engine used far less fuel than any machine previously invented. This improvement was due to the application of known physical principles. It was not an accidental result of a trial and error process but a deliberate design based on knowledge of physical laws.

Another major contribution of James Watt was his invention in 1794 of the steam indicator, a simple device which plots on a card a diagram showing the relation between steam pressure and volume as the piston moves in the cylinder. The steam indicator made possible more efficient operation of the engine based on a mathematical analysis of the pressure-volume diagram.

By 1800 Watt and his contemporaries had developed all of the mechanical devices needed for a practical reciprocating steam engine. Further progress was limited by inadequate knowledge of materials and of methods of processing materials.

The study of the properties of materials was first carried out in a satisfactory quantitative way around the middle of the seventeenth century with the work of men like Hooke, Mariotte and LaHire. The mathematician Euler became interested in the mathematical analysis of testing instruments around 1750. The proper approach to the mathematical analysis of beams and struts was outlined in 1802 by Coulomb and Rondelet. Armed with a method of predicting the behavior of materials, engineers were ready to design more powerful steam engines operating under high pressures.

By 1850 workers such as Sadi Carnot, William Thomson (Lord Kelvin) and James Prescott Joule had laid the foundation for the modern science of thermodynamics. From that time on it was increasingly possible to design an engine mathematically so as to meet specified operating conditions.

The development of engineering design techniques for the steam engine was closely paralleled by advances in the design of other mechanical devices such as weaving machines, printing presses and power tools. By the middle of the nineteenth century the design of all forms of mechanical devices was becoming more a science than an art.

In the early 1800's men began to show increasing interest in electricity, and as a result an entirely new type of human activity was created. Unlike the gears and levers of a mechanical machine, electricity could not be held in the hand and examined. No one could draw a picture of electricity and show how electricity could react on other things. However, ingenious experimenters found many ways in which the presence of electricity could be detected. The Leyden jar for the storage of static electricity had been invented in 1745 and had shown the presence of an electric charge by means of a spark. Volta had invented a battery which delivered a continuous flow of electricity in 1775. In 1820 Hans Oersted discovered that a compass needle was deflected in the presence of a wire carrying an electric current. The French mathematician Ampére repeated Oersted's work and extended the experiments to show that two parallel wires each carrying an electric current would experience forces of attraction and repulsion. In 1831 Joseph Henry in the United States discovered the basic relations between a magnetic field and a current in a wire. He quickly used these discoveries to develop the transformer. In the same year Michael Faraday in London made similar discoveries. Both Faraday and Henry built electric motors and generators. In 1837 Samuel Morse developed his telegraph using the known relationship between an electric current and the magnetic field.

In comparison with the development of mechanical devices, which involved many centuries of trial and error, the development of man's ability to design electrical instruments was rapid. The more rapid progress was due primarily to man's increasing ability to describe natural phenomena in mathematical terms. Indeed it is quite unlikely that many of the familiar advances in the field of electricity could have occurred at all if it had not been possible to describe the underlying principles in rigorous mathematical form.

One of the most amazing features of our existence is the fact that once a basic physical law has been translated into the language of mathematics, any proper manipulation of that mathematics will be exactly paralleled by corresponding changes in the physical system. Thus by manipulating the mathematics it is possible to predict the behavior of a physical system not yet constructed.

Since electricity could not be seen, men had to describe its effects mathematically. Once certain basic relationships had been so described, many others could be predicted mathematically and then subjected to experimental confirmation. By this process of mathematical production men were led to the discovery of objects which cannot be seen, and they were enabled to use such unseen objects in many ways.

The monumental mathematical formulations of James Clerk Maxwell in 1873 described the basic principles of electromagnetism and enabled the prediction of the transmission of energy without wires. The prediction was verified experimentally by Hertz in 1887 and was followed in 1895 by Marconi's development of practical wireless telegraphy.

The successful development of various electrical instruments made it possible to detect the existence of the electron and to measure its mass and charge. With this elementary particle identified, it was possible to use the electron as a means of probing for further invisible elements of matter. This search was aided and spurred by the mathematical analyses of Albert Einstein who predicted the now familiar relationship of energy to mass.

An understanding of the behavior of an electron in electric and magnetic fields led to the use of the X-ray diffractometer for the study of the structure of matter. Later, these studies of structure were aided by the electron microscope. Each experimental observation was described mathematically, and each extension in mathematical formulation led in turn to further experimental observations.

By the middle of the twentieth century it was quite obvious that man's knowledge of the universe was growing exponentially. The rate at which his knowledge was growing was proportional to his existing knowledge. The more man knows, the faster he learns. Fortunately there seems to be no limit to the capacity of the human mind to maintain the exponential growth indefinitely.

As indicated previously, the impressive expansion of man's knowledge in the first half of the twentieth century has led to the introduction of the first significant new art form in hundreds of years. This is the art of designing an instrument on the mathematical basis of the physical principles which govern its operation. In some cases there may be two phases to this endeavor: first, the mathematical analysis based on scientific principles and leading to the prediction of the behavior of a tangible device; second, the construction of the device to match in a physical way the operations previously predicted mathematically. The first phase, the mathematical analysis, is something like a poem in that it organizes diverse concepts to create a unified mental image. The second stage, the physical construction, is something akin to sculpture since it involves the skilful shaping and blending of material to form a physical object which is capable of producing an emotional response. Each phase represents a more sophisticated art form than poetry or sculpture. The two phases combined produce an entirely new concept of art.

At present, the new art of engineering design is too complex to be understood by the general public. To place a good example of this art on display in Times Square would be almost like hanging the Mona Lisa before an audience of cats and dogs. In each case the object would be seen but not appreciated. Just as the pioneers of other art forms had to die before the public could be educated to understand their work, so the engineering designer today finds himself unrecognized by most of his contemporaries. The relatively few people whose education has been sufficiently broad to include mathematics and the engineering sciences are the fortunate avant garde who can thrill to appreciation of mankind's new and greatest masterpieces.

It is always difficult to attempt to explain an example of a new art form to a person whose previous educational background does not permit him to understand the principles involved. It is like reciting a passage of the Aeneid in Latin to a person who does not understand Latin. Nevertheless, the attempt can lead to an awakening interest and subsequently to the acquisition of the knowledge needed for appreciation of the new masterpieces. Those who understand mathematics and engineering science owe it to their fellow human beings to arouse an interest in man's greatest works. Teachers of mathematics and science share this responsibility and privilege.

As an example of a masterpiece of engineering design consider the amazingly simple tunnel diode and its use in an oscillating circuit. The background of "scientific culture" which made it possible for this device to be created and so used goes back to the Leyden jar of van Musschenbroek (1745), the battery of Alessandro Volta (1775), the electromagnet of Jospeh Henry (1831), the mathematical equations of Maxwell (1873), and the oscillating circuits of Hertz (1887). The mathematics of Maxwell predicted that energy could be transmitted through space if an electric current could be made to oscillate at a high frequency. Mathematical analysis also showed that under certain conditions current could be made to oscillate in a circuit consisting of a Leyden jar (or capacitor as we now call it) an electromagnet (or inductor) and a battery in series. The wires and components of such a circuit contain resistance. According to the mathematical analysis, the current should oscillate if the resistance, inductance and capacitance are related by the inequality $R < \sqrt{4L/c}$. Normally the resistance of the circuit to the flow of current is too high to permit oscillation. However, if some form of negative resistance can be introduced to counteract the positive resistance of the circuit, oscillation will result.

The concept of negative resistance is difficult to grasp. Positive resistance in a circuit is like friction which impedes the flow of electricity. Negative resistance must be less than no friction at all. It must in some way help rather than hinder the flow of current. With positive resistance an increase in current can be attained only by increasing the driving force (electromotive force). With negative resistance, an increase in current must be accompanied by a drop in the driving force. Thus a negative resistance corresponds to a negative slope in the curve of driving force vs current. If a device can be found which exhibits such a negative slope it can be used as a negative resistance.

In an ordinary conductor, such as a piece of copper wire, some of the electrons in the atoms which compose the wire are free to move in the presence of an electric field. When a battery is connected across the wire it sets up an electric field and causes the electrons to move. Since the electrons are electrically charged, their movement constitutes an electric current. The greater the voltage or driving force of the battery, the greater the current. In other words the current is directly proportional to the driving force. The electrons moving through the wire encounter friction which is called resistance. In a copper wire this resistance is always positive, and hence an increase in driving force is always required to produce an increase in current.

In an insulator such as glass the electrons in the atoms are tightly bound in what are known as completely filled shells of energy levels. Very little current can be made to flow through an insulator unless electromotive forces are applied of sufficient magnitude to break down the structure of the material.

Lying between conductors and insulators are a few substances known as semi-conductors. In a semi-conductor the electrons in the atoms are tightly bound in completely filled energy levels. However, as can be shown mathematically, it is possible for some of these electrons to move to vacant energy levels under the influence of moderate electromotive forces without damaging the structure of the material. The few electrons which move into vacant levels can then be set into motion to form an electric current. For a given driving force this current is less than that which would be attained in a conductor.

In some forms of semi-conductors, the movement of an electron into a vacant energy level has the effect of leaving a hole in the crystalline structure of the material. Since the electron bears a negative electric charge, the hole is in effect a positive charge. Under the influence of the driving force this positive hole will move in a direction opposite to that of the negative electron and will thus produce the same type of electric current. A semi-conductor in which most of the current is caused by the movement of positive holes is called "p-type." One in which most of the current is carried by negative electrons is called "n-type."

It is possible to design and synthesize either p-type or n-type semi-conductors. It is also possible to produce both types in one bar of stock material. For example, germanium can be made a p-type semi-conductor by adding slight amounts of gallium, and it can be made into n-type by adding arsenic. By proper control, it is possible to construct a tiny piece of germanium in which the two types are separated by a well-defined junction or boundary.

Such a junction-type semi-conductor exhibits very interesting directional properties. In general, there is a low resistance to current flow in one direction and a high resistance in the other. However, for narrow junctions both resistances are positive.

A man named Leo Esaki predicted mathematically that by proper design of the thickness of the junction and of the concentrations of the impurities, the resistance in the low direction could be positive for low driving force, negative for medium driving forces and positive again for higher forces. The intermediate range of negative resistance was explained as a tunnelling effect whereby electrons could tunnel through the barrier at the junction. There is no simple way to understand this phenomenon except by mathematical analysis employing the most advanced concepts of quantum mechanics. The principle which Esaki predicted has been used to create a semi-conducting device having a negative resistance. It is called the Esaki diode or the tunnel diode.

Now returning to the problem of producing oscillations, here was one answer to the need for a negative resistance. By combining the tunnel diode with an inductor and a capacitor it is possible to produce the desired oscillations and thus to perform many useful operations.

The tunnel diode is a lump of metal with two wires attached to it. Specimens have been made which are smaller than the diameter of a human hair. This tiny device uses the movement of things that we cannot see, driven by invisible electric forces, to perform a vast variety of operations useful to mankind. It is one of the masterpieces of the human race.

It is fascinating to follow the masterful ways in which

engineers have combined many such miniature works of art like the tunnel diode into vast and complex electro-mechanical systems which operate beautifully as unified organisms. The truly educated person of the twentieth century can respond emotionally to such contemplation with more excitement and satisfaction than has ever been possible to his predecessors or to his narrowly educated contemporaries.

Those who are teaching mathematics and engineering science are the most privileged servants of mankind in mid-twentieth century because they are providing the liberal education needed to appreciate our greatest masterpieces of man's most sophisticated art.

THE USEFULNESS OF THE IMPOSSIBLE

BILLY E. GOETZ

What Professor Goetz here calls the "impossible" in mathematics refers, of course, to the abstract nature of mathematical concepts and relations. They are impossible because they are ideal or "perfect." But by virtue of their perfection, they are amenable to the laws of logic and internal consistency, and thus we can think about them in rigorous terms.

The aim of mathematics is "to think rigorously whatever is rigorously thinkable or whatever may become rigorously thinkable in course of the upward striving and refining evolution of ideas." Thus wrote the late Professor C. J. Keyser, distinguished philosopher, mathematician, and humanist. He had in mind the bearings or "applications" of mathematics upon Science, Art, Philosophy, Jurisprudence and Religion. Goetz's delightful essay spells out this thesis in a unique way.

Professor Goetz is professor of Industrial Management at the Massachusetts Institute of Technology.

The Usefulness of the Impossible*

A STRAIGHT LINE has no width, no depth, no wiggles, and no ends.

There are no straight lines. We have ideas about these non-existent impossibilities: we even draw pictures of them. But they do not exist.

Ask a draftsman to draw a straight line. Place his product under a microscope. Observe the variable width; the darkness and lightness which mark its varying depth; the wiggles, both lateral and vertical, where the line plunges and climbs and wiggles among the fibers. Put the microscope away and observe the ends of the line where it runs off the paper. Finally, contemplate the curvature of space.

A straight line hasn't even a definition. Heath, in his *Thirteen Books of Euclid's Elements,* discusses the problem. Before Euclid, Paramenides has stated "straight is whatever has its middle in front of both ends." Euclid defined a straight line as "a line which lies evenly with the points on itself." Heron, in the first century, A.D., suggested "a line stretched to the utmost." Equally old, although restated by Leibniz and put into the following form by Gauss, is: "The line in which lie all points that, during the revolution of a part of space about two fixed points, maintain their position unchanged. . . ." While this may seem definitions aplenty, the modern view as expressed by Pfleiderer is: "It seems as though the notion of a straight line, owing to its simplicity, cannot be explained by any regular definition which does not introduce words already containing in themselves, by implication, the notion to be defined, as though it were impossible, if a person does not already know what the term straight here means, to teach it to him unless by putting before him in some way a picture or a drawing of it."

A point has no dimensions, no existence, and no definition. A picture of a point is a ragged area of uncertain extent on a rough surface. By refining the picture, the area diminishes.

* Reprinted from American Association of University Professors *Bulletin*, vol. 42, pp. 275–287, 1956. By permission of the author and the editor of the *Bulletin*.

Finally, we can refine no more. We place the portraits side by side in the sequence of successive refinement. Then we point far to the side and say, "The picture that belongs there, where refinement has been carried to the ultimate and the dimensions have entirely vanished; that picture, if it existed, would be a true dimensionless point."

Euclid lists twenty-three definitions which define more than twenty-three figments of the imagination. Next he postulates an ability to draw straight lines from point to point, to project these straight lines indefinitely in either direction, and to draw circles; all manifest impossibilities. He assumes all right angles are equal, although there are no right angles. And he includes the famous postulate of parallels, by denying which Riemann created the geometry of curved space. Lastly, Euclid introduces five "common notions" as axioms; that is, as self-evident truths; the very first of which is impossible, let alone true. "Things equal to the same thing are equal to each other." No two real things are precisely equal. The common equal is doubly doubtful. It is an impossible ideal which can be approached only imaginatively.

He who protests that this is a quibble, that for practical purposes equals do exist, merely impales himself on the other horn of a dilemma. In a chapter on Number in his *Aspects of Science,* Tobias Dantzig tells of two bars, *A* and *B,* so nearly the same length as to defeat all attempts to ascertain which is the longer. Practically, they are of equal length. Another bar, *C,* is so nearly the same length as *B* as to defy all attempts to show a difference. Practically, *B* and *C* are also of equal length. But when *A* is compared with *C,* there is no difficulty in proving that *C* is longer than *A.* So if we deal with practical equalities, things may be equal to the same thing without being equal to each other.

The whole of geometry is consciously, wilfully, deliberately antagonistic to reality. In classical geometry, the compass and straight edge are allowed, the ruler forbidden. The compass and straight edge are both mystical, for they produce true circles and lines. The ruler is a practical tool used by artisans and beneath the dignity of a Greek philosopher-mathematician. Modern geometry has exceeded the purity of the ancients. It deals with points which are not points but vague unspecified items; lines which are not lines but classes of items; and planes that are not planes but classes of classes. In some modern geometries, straight lines are distorted geodesics twisting and wriggling in a warped and changing space. In modern physics, these writhing monsters are chopped into a large, but finite, number of tiny, but not infinitesimal, discontinuous, discrete quanta. This is as near as we can get to "real" straight lines!

Nor is geometry the black sheep of mathematics. All mathematics carries the family taint; all mathematics is a gigantic tussle with nonexistent impossibilties. We are cautioned not to add poems and railroad trains, or to subtract centimeters from miles. Without referring to what is added on the balance sheets of business enterprises, let us merely note that if one ought not to add apples and bananas, one probably shouldn't add Jonathans and Rome Beauties, or big apples and little ones, or 1929 dollars and 1932 dollars. If we are to add at all, we must add unlikes, in violation of all mathematical regulations.

I shall not attempt to prove that mathematics is useful. I will admit it and so save myself the trouble of proving that here is a great and respected discipline where all is impossible and yet much is useful. The usefulness largely flows from the impossibility. Mathematical concepts have been simplified and generalized until they describe an imaginative world no part of which could possibly exist outside men's minds. But their simplicity and generality have made them amenable to the laws of logic. We can think about them with sufficient rigor to build a truly impressive edifice, much of which translates into physics and engineering.

II

Truth to the mathematician merely means freedom from internal inconsistencies. All mathematics begins with a set of axioms. Any set of axioms is as valid as any other as long as it avoids contradictory assumptions. Physics supposedly labors under the additional handicap of the experimental method. Its assumptions must be consistent with the readings of its meters and its gauges. The superstructure based on these assumptions must submit to experimental verification. As a result, the novice believes physics describes objective reality. Only mathematics enjoys a greater reputation for the profundity and pervasiveness of its Truths.

Physics, too, is plagued by questionable tactics. Laws proved untrue are easily rescued by adding terms. For example, Boyle's law was found untrue for high pressures and low temperatures. Van der Waal argued that it held precisely only for a perfect gas with point molecules; that as the molecules of a real gas crowded closer together the error became more noticeable. He saved Boyle's law by introducing another term to take care of the size of the molecules. If more refined experiments reveal further discrepancies, the law may be rescued again by introducing corrections for the velocities of the molecules, or for their nationalities. If the velocities won't explain the hypothetical inaccuracies of the law, the physicist may try accelerations or differential equations of still another order. If a proportional law doesn't fit, he can try inverse proportions, or squares, or exponents. Somewhere he can find a physical measurement which seems to have some kind of mathematical relation to the observed deviations, and all such troubles will surely yield to the same treatment.[1]

Newton's laws of dynamics exhibit a refinement of the technique. Nowhere has anyone ever seen a body continue moving in a straight line with uniform velocity. Nor has anyone ever seen a body at rest remain at rest. Indeed, we do not even know what the words "at rest" mean. I quote Dantzig loosely and out of context: "How can a bird fly in a straight line and at constant speed in the teeth of gravity? The answer is that the *resistance* of the air balances the gravitational pull. How can a ball roll down an inclined path at constant velocity instead of constantly accelerating? The friction of the surface accounts for this. Why do the particles of a solid body stay put, instead of flying asunder under the action of gravity? *Cohesive internal forces* keep them together. Whenever and wherever a violation of the principle of inertia is observed, it is sufficient to invoke some reaction to have the difficulty vanish, as though by magic." The accountant has a nasty name for the technique. He calls it "plugging" to force a balance.

From plugging the accounts, it is only a short step to the next refinement. The physicist avoids the need of a rescuing plug by making his laws true by definition. I quote Poincaré's great work, *Science and Hypothesis:* "The principles of dynamics at first appeared to us as experimental truths; but we have been obliged to use them as definitions. It is by definition that force is equal to the product of mass by acceleration; here, then, is a principle which is henceforth beyond the reach of any further experiment. It is in the same way by definition that action is equal to reaction." Having set up his definitions, the physicist calibrates his instruments accordingly. Having defined force as proportional to acceleration, and having chosen some force as a unit, he doubles the acceleration and marks his force meter two at the point indicated. Ever after, whenever he measures with the instruments so created, his findings bear out his definitions; his laws become absolutely true.

The culmination of the technique is the creation of so anthropomorphic a cosmology as to be beyond the ability of men to prove or disprove it. Eddington states the case thus: "We have found a strange footprint on the shores of the unknown. We have devised profound theories, one after another, to account for its origin. At last we have succeeded in reconstructing the creature that made the footprint, And lo! it is our own." Dantzig goes farther. I quote at length:

"For however phantastic a universe our mind may conceive, our mind can also conceive it peopled by species, endowed with consciousness, intelligence and mobility, which in the course of time would arrive at a cosmology identical with our own.

"Seeking permanence in the shifting chaos of their perceptions, these beings would eventually discover in their environment bodies which would behave in relative unison to their own. Accepting these bodies for rigid standards, they would proceed to survey and measure the universe with their aid. Singling out some cyclic phenomena which recur in relative synchrony to each other, and to their own physiological processes, these beings would finish by identifying these temporal series with their own stream of consciousness. Convinced that their universe was independent of their consciousness, they would affirm the objective character of their conception of time, and proceeding beyond the narrow confines of their own experience, they would extend their conception to the world at large, conceiving the latter as floating with absolute uniformity on the stream of duration. And transferring to their universe their own physiological and psychological attributes, they would fill space with bristling forces and shackle history to a causal chain."

As with mathematics, I propose to assume that physics is useful, although I feel some doubt has been cast upon its objective validity. The rigorous exclusion of all nonmeasurable phenomena, and the careful formulation of its definitions and axioms as the calibrations of the instruments to be used in the experimental verification of physical laws, have simplified and generalized physics along the lines of the mathematical model. This has added immensely to its precision, to its power, and to its usefulness.

III

Mathematics and physics are theoretical. Let us turn from abstraction and generalization to practical application. Engineering is as riddled with impossibility as mathematics or physics. Of course, engineering is full of mathematics and physics; they are the basic sciences. But I do not rest my case here. Engineering data are as impossible as engineering's mathematical method. Engineering data are average values, usually treated in engineering calculations as absolutes. According to Mills' *Materials of Construction,* structural steel has an elastic limit of 35,000 pounds per square inch, a tensile strength of 65,000 pounds per square inch, and a modulus of elasticity of 30,000,000 pounds per square inch. No standard deviations are given. Such values are found only in the inexact, semi-scientific disciplines of biology, psychology and economics.[2]

In calculating the distortion of bridge members, the engineer implicitly assumes constant cross-sections, uniform crystal structures, and homogeneous chemical composition from end to end of each beam. Anyone who has seen the scale peel off an ingot as it goes through the rolls knows the constant cross-section is a crude fiction. Heat treatment and the working of steel so change crystal structures as to make the assumption of uniformity in ordinary rolled beams heroic indeed.

However, the engineer is a practical fellow. While his equations assume a 35,000-pound elastic limit in a prefectly uniform beam, he does not. To keep his bridges from falling when these assumptions err on the wrong side, he typically designs them to carry seven times the expected maximum load. This makes bridges expensive but safe. The engineer can boast that they seldom fall. Yet engineers are modest braggarts. The multiplier used to assure safety has been rechristened the "factor of ignorance."[3]

IV

In mathematics, physics, and engineering, we see that the impossible may be useful—at least as a calculating device.

My purpose so far is not to pillory these respectable and useful disciplines, but rather to throw a mantle of respectability over the shady dealings I am about to perpetrate. I propose to apply the method of the impossible calculating device to the science of economics. As in mathematics, we begin with a few impossible assumptions; go where we can; and introduce further impossible assumptions whenever we get stuck.

Let us assume all men are alike; are exclusively gain motivated; know all the facts; always behave logically; act as completely independent social atoms; and can transfer from job to job or place to place instantly and without loss or regret. There are no such men.

Let us assume that such economic men live in a world of diminishing returns and have their sole intercourse in free markets. A free market, by definition, involves private property; no collusion among buyers or sellers; instantaneous complete communication among all participants; and no coercion—every trade must be wholly voluntary on both sides. There are no such markets.

These assumptions may be redundant; they may even be in conflict—surely the legal part of my audience will permit such economic license. Probably such an economic world, so peopled, would disintegrate through self-generated centrifugal tendencies. There is no religion and no tradition to hold them together. There is assumed to be a state which enforces contracts, prevents stealing and cheating, and preserves the peace of the realm.

Still seeking simplicity, we create an imaginary world for these imaginary people; a new continent in which every square foot of surface has the same fertility, drainage, temperature, rainfall and sunlight; following the same unvarying pattern year after year.

Let us place one of our standard economic men on our new continent. If he farms a single square inch, his product will be nil. If he attempts to farm the whole continent, he will be too busy walking to plant, cultivate, or harvest. Somewhere between these limits his product reaches a maximum—the goal of the economic man. We will call this optimum area a plot, and will assume exactly a thousand such plots on the continent. We will further assume that one man can produce 80 tons of product per year on one such plot. If he cultivates more or less land, his annual product will be less than 80 tons. By the law of diminishing returns, we know that he can produce more than 40 tons on half a plot, for he can weed, cultivate, and irrigate more intensively. Let us assume that on half a plot he could produce 70 tons and on a third of a plot 60 tons.

Let us add economic men. Each takes possession of a plot and reaps a harvest of 80 tons annually until we reach a population of a thousand. Then all the plots have been pre-empted; the West has been won; the frontier is closed. We add the thousand and first man and ominous social changes take place. He becomes the first of a landless wage-earning class. Since two men on one plot, or one on each of two half-plots, can produce 140 tons, the newcomer adds 60 tons to the product; and that is the maximum wage any land owner will pay. The free market and competition among land owners will drive the wage offered up to, but never beyond, 60 tons.

Now we add more economic men to our mythical continent. No significant economic change occurs until the two thousand and first man arrives. He must cut his price to take a job away from one of the earlier immigrants. But there will always remain one man unemployed and underquoting the prevailing wage rate until it is hammered down to 40 tons. Since three men on a plot can produce 180 tons, the third man adds 40 tons to the gross income of the land owner and can be hired at that rate without firing his predecessor.

Let us add a few more economic men to get safely beyond the critical number and then review and take stock. If we add a man, the total social product increases 40 tons, as does the gross income of the owner of the land on which he works; and this fixes the wage rate, for no owner will give more and competition among owners makes it unnecessary for the laborer to take less. If a landowner retires, his gross income falls from 180 to 140 tons—evidently he gets 40 tons for his own work. Having retired, he gets a gross income of 140 and pays each of two men 40 tons, leaving 60 for himself. This, then, is the earning power, or rent, of the land. Suppose we add a plot to the continent. Then a man will leave each of two plots on which three men have been working to take up the new land. Each of the plots they leave produces 40 tons less per year. But the new plot produces 140 tons, a net gain of 60 evidently imputable to the land rather than to the labor. Thus whether we add or subtract land or laborers, we find that the wage rate comes out 40 and the rent 60. The ratio of land to labor fixes both wages and rent.

V

Now we add a spellbinder. He promises more *Lebensraum* and a higher standard of living for the Master Race. He is elected *Führer* and begins to make good on his promises. By blaming Jews for the desperately low wages, he starts a pogrom, which reduces the pressure of population on the soil, and thus tends to raise the wages of the survivors. He adds to the *Lebensraum* by conquering neighboring lands, but he must take them relatively empty or the population pressure will continue unaltered. He bombs civilians, ostensibly to break morale and win a war. He relocates whole populations to make peoples conform to boundaries. He dispossesses the private owners of conquered lands to give the Master Race the product imputed by the market to land as well as the product of their own toil.

Or the champion of the propertyless masses can employ emergency relief and boondoggling make-work schemes to draw labor from the competitive market until the marginal productivity, and the wage level, of privately employed labor is raised to any desired standard. This will be expensive, but an unbalanced national budget will temporarily finance any requirements of the program which cannot be met by soaking the rich.

A union leader's powers are more circumscribed. He, *der Führer,* and the Great Democratic Leader could raise living standards by a program for increasing the productivity of labor. This way to a better life requires thoughtful intelligence and, consequently, seldom appeals to the purveyors of emotion whom we perennially elect as dictators, presidents, and union leaders. The path of restricted supply requires less effort and intelligence, usually resting on force, which such people understand better. To the union boss, this means a closed shop, enforced by strikes and picketing. But the closed shop will not reduce the ratio of labor to other factors of production unless membership in the union is sharply restricted. This is usually accomplished by high dues and initiation fees, or by arduous apprenticeship requirements, preferably the former, as these enable the maintenance of elaborate country estates. All methods of restricting entrance to a trade are anti-social, as they push labor from the more remunerative vocations into the relatively overcrowded nonunion occupations. However, the union members benefit by higher wages and cheerfully re-elect their business manager. The exploited consumer and the depressed labor in nonunion occupations have no vote in union elections.

Real leaders in a real world may discover other opportunities for raising wages. The premises of our theory do not accurately describe the real world. Consequently, real wages may fall below the marginal productivity of labor, the wage rate for our impossible world of economic freedom. Laborers are not economic men. They do not know all the facts. Unions or governments may provide information about opportunities in other companies and towns. Laborers cannot transfer easily from job to job or place to place without loss or regret. Moving costs money, and union or government may advance money to finance such moves. Moving breaks social ties, and the union may facilitate entry to the social life of the new community. Nor do laborers think logically. The employee-employer relationship involves much besides wages and hours; much which individual laborers are prone to overlook. So government and union have a role to play in settling secondary matters, such as safety provisions, conditions of work, vacations, seniority, and many more.

The market is not always coercion-free as assumed. A single large company operating in a small company town is likely to be a monopsony. Trade associations may rig the labor market. Government and union may go in for trust busting; or the union may organize supply to confront monopsony with monopoly.

VI

Perhaps it will be contended that I have not demonstrated the usefulness of the impossible; that I have arrived at the same self-evident conclusions everyone holds without recourse to such theoretical analysis. I do not believe so. Laborers and unions have long been committed to the lump-of-work fallacy. They have been fearful of doing too much, of working too fast, and so causing unemployment. This restriction of output makes men less valuable to employers and society, and so depresses wages. It is disadvantageous for employer, employee and community. The restriction on entrance to a trade undoubtedly raises wages in the restricted field at the cost of depressing wages elsewhere. Those damaged by exclusion have concentrated their efforts on establishing restricted monopolistic fields of their own. Nowhere have the disinherited fought for their American heritage—the right to choose their vocation.

Unions have blindly fought for higher wage rates without considering consequences. They have assumed that a certain lump of work had to be performed regardless of the price charged for it. The building trades in particular have been successful; so successful that there was almost no building construction for ten years during the Great Depression of the 1930's—surely a potent demonstration that buyers buy less at high prices than at lower. A war demand with government financing surmounted the barrier of high construction costs, and factory building boomed. Impending inflation made bonds, insurance, and money-hoarding unsatisfactory vehicles for savings. The shadow of new taxes made corporate securities uncertain and undesirable. What was one to do with his money, if any? In spite of construction costs, the accumulating housing shortage, together with the ominous threat of inflation and the hazardous nature of every other form of investment, have produced a residential building boom.

Yet much of our last unlamented Great Depression was due to absurd costs of construction. A large part of our unemployment was in the building trades, which were almost altogether unemployed. Hourly wages in these occupations were higher in 1934 than in 1929, although practically all other prices, particularly rents, were from 25% to 50% lower. Let us return to our impossible calculating devices to seek an explanation for such mad behavior.

By our assumption of diminishing utility, buyers will be ready to buy more buildings if their prices fall. Given one big industrial union, a wage reduction would result in a comparable reduction in building costs, which would result in substantially more construction and employment. In general, labor will gain more in employment than it loses in lowered hourly rates up to the point at which the market is cleared and unemployment vanishes. The industrial union could learn this lesson by bitter experience and the mad spiral of rising costs and declining construction would cease.

We have trade unions in the building industry, and a trade union cannot learn this lesson, because it doesn't apply to a trade union. If any union, acting independently, reduces its wage rate, total building costs are negligibly reduced and building volume insignificantly increased. The union members gain little in increased employment and lose much in lowered wage rates. Meantime, all the other unions benefit equally by the increased building activity without reducing their rates.

Conversely, if any one trade raises its rate, building costs increase a little and construction activity decreases a little. All building labor shares the decrease in employment, but one union alone reaps the advantage of a higher wage rate. Consequently, they gain more in the increased rate than they lose in the decreased employment. Under the assumed conditions, if each union acts independently, they will take turns raising their rates. The raises will cumulate and the total impact on building activity will put an end to the industry; labor will have committed economic suicide. If the unions should coalesce into one big industrial union, effect would follow cause promptly and simply. The leaders and the members might learn and the industry might not throw more than a million men on relief. Theory supports the C.I.O. against the A.F. of L. in the building trades unless the inter-union councils gain power and finally become the bargaining agent for all member unions acting in unison.

VII

I will conclude with one last example of the usefulness of the impossible in avoiding derailment of a train of analysis. It will show why a man may successfully operate a business and still hold dangerous political ideas. A successful budgeteer friend of mine believes what he sees and will have no truck with the impossible. He believes in induction to the total exclusion of deduction. His ideas of the causes and cure of depressions are simple: All industries which have organized to agree on prices and control their markets are generally profitable. The industries which follow the old tradition of free competition are in chaotic condition and are chronically depressed. To achieve universal prosperity, we should compel the competitors to organize, to cease cutting each others' throats. This was, of course, the NRA program.

We have already seen how labor monopolists gain advantage at the expense of unorganized consumers and laborers; how restricted entrance maintains wages in one field by further depressing wages elsewhere. Universal organization prevents any group from achieving prosperity by monopoly because it would leave no one to exploit. All market rigging by unions and by industries involves restricted outputs. Normally the organized steel industry seldom operates above 60% or 70% of capacity and makes a profit at any rate above 45%. The unorganized argicultural industries operate near 100% all the time and are chronically depressed. I say the steel industry has behaved anti-socially, and should be subjected to enough policing to enforce competition. If this proves impossible, the steel industry should be socialized. On the other hand, agriculture has done its social best. Aside from conservation measures, it should be let alone.

Suppose all industries are forced to disorganize, to allow markets to be free. Then all would operate at capacity, and prices would be cut until the market was cleared. The maximum production would be maintained and consumed; the standard of living would reach the highest possible level.

Suppose all industries follow my friend's advice and organize to control their markets, to bring order out of chaos. Then all restrict outputs, all operate well below capacity. The total product is much less, the population remains the same, and the standard of living must be substantially lowered.

We have seen how useful the impossible has become in mathematics, physics, and engineering. If the same simplified, generalized calculating technique be applied to economics, the solutions to real problems will be sharp and clear. Perhaps this will make the appeal to emotion unpopular and unprofitable. Then we may have done with artificial shortages imposed by such government schemes as NRA and AAA, by monopolistic combines acting in collusion to restrict output and rig markets, and by unions restricting entrance and murdering industries.

NOTES

[1] Physicists tell me that this paragraph isn't fair.

[2] This is true only of elementary works.

[3] Although the engineer claims to *know*, and patronizingly refers to business judgments as wild, inaccurate guesses, the facts do not seem to bear out his claims to precision. Business men seem to be almost exactly as ignorant as engineers. Many business men will not make improvements unless they believe savings of the first two years will return the original investment. If we assume 7% is a reasonable return on the owner's investment, this provides a "factor of ignorance" of almost precisely seven.

SCIENCE AND FINITUDE

William Barrett

The world today is living in a dynamic period of transition. It is a transition which involves uncertainty and insecurity not only in the sphere of political, social and religious convictions, but also in the realm of scientific and mathematical thought. The accompanying confusion concerning traditional values and beliefs has led, in no small measure, to the rise of modern existentialism.

This thesis is ably explored by William Barrett in his book on existential philosophy. In a chapter aptly entitled "The Encounter with Nothingness" he discusses the decline of religion, the dissolution of society, and the tenuous foundations upon which modern science rests. The following excerpt from this chapter deals with the intrinsic limitations of man as mathematician. Disconcerting though these limitations may be, they are indubitable hallmarks of the mathematics of the mid-twentieth century.

Mr. Barrett is professor of philosophy at New York University.

Science and Finitude*

. . . EXISTENTIAL philosophy embodies the self-questioning of the time, seeking to reorient itself to its own historical destiny. Indeed, the whole problematic of Existentialism unfolds from this historical situation. Alienation and estrangement; a sense of the basic fragility and contingency of human life; the impotence of reason confronted with the depths of existence; the threat of Nothingness, and the solitary and unsheltered condition of the individual before this threat. One can scarcely subordinate these problems logically one to another; each participates in all the others, and they all circulate around a common center. A single atmosphere pervades them all like a chilly wind: the radical feeling of human finitude. The limitless horizons into which man looked at the time of the Renaissance have at last contracted. Oddly enough, man's discovery that he himself is finite through and through—is so, one might say, from the inside out—comes at a time when there seem no longer to be any limits to his technological conquest of nature. But the truth about man is never to be found in one quality that opposes another, but in both qualities at once; and so his weakness is only one side of the coin, his power the other. A recognition of limits, of boundaries, may be the only thing that prevents power from dizzy collapse.

But, it might be argued, what makes Western civilization unique is its possession of science, and in science we find uniform and continuous progress without limits. Research goes on, its results are rich and positive, and these are brought together in ever wider and more inclusive systems. There would seem, in this process, to be no contracting of horizons either in fact or in possibility. In a certain sense this is true, and yet science in the twentieth century has come up with answers which make the ambitions of rationalism seem overweening, and which themselves suggest that man must

* From *Irrational Man: A Study in Existential Philosophy*, by William Barrett. Copyright © 1958 by William Barrett. Reprinted by permission and courtesy of Doubleday & Company, Inc., New York, and Heinemann Educational Books Ltd., London.

redefine his traditional concept of reason. It would be unlikely if this were otherwise, for scientists too are men and
therefore participate in the collective psyche as well as help
fashion it. Religion, social forms, science, and art are modes
in which man exists; and the more we come to recognize the
temporal being of man the more we must recognize a unity
within and behind all these modes in which that temporal
existence finds its expression.

Science too—and within its own authentic sphere—has
come up against the fact of human finitude. That this has
happened within science itself, and not in the philosophizing
about science, makes the discovery more authentic and
momentous. The anthropological sciences, and particularly
modern depth psychology, have shown us that human reason
is the long historical fabrication of a creature, man, whose
psychic roots still extend downward into the primeval soil.
These discoveries of the irrational, however, lie outside reason itself; they are stubborn obstacles to the use of reason in
our lives, but obstacles which the confirmed rationalist might
still hope to circumvent by a cleverer use of that very tool,
reason. The more decisive limitations are those that have
shown up *within* the workings of reason, in the more rigorous sciences of physics and mathematics. The most advanced
of Western sciences, physics and mathematics, have in our
time become paradoxical: that is, they have arrived at the
state where they breed paradoxes for reason itself. More
than a hundred and fifty years ago the philosopher Kant attempted to show that there were ineluctable limits to reason;
but the Western mind, positivistic to the core, could be expected to take such a conclusion seriously only when it
showed up in the findings of science. Science has in this century, with the discoveries of Heisenberg in physics, and
Gödel in mathematics, at last caught up with Kant.

Heisenberg's Principle of Indeterminacy shows that there
are essential limits to our ability to know and predict physical states of affairs, and opens up to us a glimpse of a nature
that may at bottom be irrational and chaotic—at any rate,
our knowledge of it is limited so that we cannot know this
not to be the case. This finding marks an end to the old
dream of physicists who, motivated by a thoroughly rational
prejudice, thought that reality must be predictable through
and through. The figure of the Laplacian Demon was a very
striking symbol of this: Imagine, says Laplace, a Being who

knows the position and momentum of every particle in the universe, together with the laws of motion governing such particles; such a Being would be able to predict all subsequent states of the universe. Physicists can no longer operate on such cryptotheological faiths, but must take their predictability only where and to the extent that it exhibits itself in experience.

The situation in physics is made more paradoxical by Bohr's Principle of Complementarity, according to which the electron must be regarded both as a wave and as a particle, according to its context. The application of these contradictory designations would have seemed thoroughly illogical to a nineteenth-century physicist. Indeed, some physicists have suggested a new form of logic, from which the classic law of the Excluded Middle (either A or not A) would be dropped; and when new forms of logic are being constructed, one can only conclude that the nature of what is and what is not rational stands open to doubt. In practice, the Principle of Complementarity sets a rigorous limit upon the observations of physics: As one physicist, von Pauli, puts it, *"I can choose to observe one experimental set-up, A, and ruin B, or choose to observe B and ruin A. I cannot choose not to ruin one of them."* Here the language is perfectly appropriate to the pathos of knowledge in every area in life: we know one thing at the cost of not knowing something else, and it is simply not the case that we can choose to know everything at once. What is remarkable is that here, at the very farthest reaches of precise experimentation, in the most rigorous of the natural sciences, the ordinary and banal fact of our human limitations emerges.

Gödel's findings seem to have even more far-reaching consequences, when one considers that in the Western tradition, from the Pythagoreans and Plato onward, mathematics as the very model of intelligibility has been the central citadel of rationalism. Now it turns out that even in his most precise science—in the province where his reason had seemed omnipotent—man cannot escape his essential finitude: every system of mathematics that he constructs is doomed to incompleteness. Gödel has shown that mathematics contains insoluble problems, and hence can never be formalized in any complete system. This means, in other words, that mathematics can never be turned over to a giant computing machine; it will always be unfinished, and therefore mathematicians—the human beings who construct mathematics—will always be in business. The human element here rises above the machine: mathematics is unfinished as is any human life.

But since mathematics can never be completed, it might be argued that Gödel's finding shows us that there are no limits to mathematical knowledge. True, in one sense; but in another sense it set a more drastic limitation upon mathematical knowledge, since mathematicians now know they can never, formally speaking, reach rock bottom; in fact, there is no rock bottom, since mathematics has no self-subsistent reality independent of the human activity that mathematicians carry on. And if human reason can never reach rock bottom (complete systematization) in mathematics, it is not likely to reach it anywhere else. There is no System possible for human existence, Kierkegaard said a century ago, differing with Hegel, who wished to enclose reality within a completely rational structure; the System is impossible for mathematics, Gödel tells us today. In practice, the fact that there is no rock bottom means that the mathematician can never prove the consistency of mathematics except by using means that are shakier than the system he is trying to prove consistent. Mathematics thus cannot escape finally the uncertainty that attaches to any human enterprise.

The situation is all the more vexing since mathematicians in the last half century have come up with some very troublesome paradoxes. Mathematics is like a ship in mid-ocean that has sprung certain leaks (paradoxes); the leaks have been temporarily plugged, but our reason can never guarantee that the ship will not spring others. This human insecurity in what had been the most secure of the disciplines of rationality marks a new turn in Western thinking. When the mathematician Hermann Weyl exclaims, "We have tried to storm Heaven, and we have only succeeded in piling up the tower of Babel," he is giving passionate expression to the collapse of human *hubris;* and we can be sure that mathematics has at last been returned to its rightful status as an activity or mode of being of finite man.

The concurrence of these various discoveries in time is extraordinary. Heidegger published his *Being and Time,* a somber and rigorous meditation on human finitude, in 1927. In the same year Heisenberg gave to the world his Principle of Indeterminacy. In 1929 the mathematician Skolem published a theorem which some mathematicians now think almost as remarkable as Gödel's: that even the elementary number system cannot be categorically formalized. In 1931 appeared Gödel's epoch-making discovery. When events run parallel this way, when they occur so close together in time, but independently of each other and in diverse fields, we are tempted to conclude that they are not mere "meaningless" coincidences but very meaningful symptoms. The whole mind of the time seems to be inclining in one direction.

What emerges from these separate strands of history is an image of man himself that bears a new, stark, more nearly naked, and more questionable aspect. The contraction of man's horizons amounts to a denudation, a stripping down, of this being who has now to confront himself at the center of all his horizons. The labor of modern culture, wherever it has been authentic, has been a labor of denudation. A return to the sources; "to the things themselves," as Husserl puts it; toward a new truthfulness, the casting away of ready-made presuppositions and empty forms—these are some of the slogans under which this phase in history has presented itself. Naturally enough, much of this stripping down must appear as the work of destruction, as revolutionary or even "negative": a being who has become thoroughly questionable to himself must also find questionable his relation to the total past which in a sense he represents.

THE LARGER HUMAN WORTH OF MATHEMATICS

Robert D. Carmichael

What is this thing called mathematics? What is the secret of its irresistible attraction for man? Concerning the first question, we note that the ancient word manthanein *means "to learn," and that the Greek root* mathesis *means "knowledge." Thus to want to know for the sake of knowing, is merely to be human. Mathematics—for its own sake—is wanting a particular kind of knowing, self-contained knowing, if we may be permitted to put it that way, or autonomous thinking.*

When we have said what kind of knowing, we have in large measure also answered the second question. Freedom; Order; Harmony; Beauty; Austerity; Elegance; Certainty: these the soul of man forever seeks with unconquerable spirit. In mathematics he finds them.

Profoundly moved by the human side of mathematics, Professor Carmichael here succeeds in capturing this subtle quality through his capacity for introspection, his wide acquaintance with mathematics, his sensitivity to poetry, and his complete unaffectedness.

The Larger Human Worth of Mathematics*

MATHEMATICAL THOUGHT has exercised over my spirit a fascination which is far-reaching in its effect upon my activity and happiness. It is not an easy matter to present the characteristics of this thought to one who has not been initiated into the remarkable secrets of the science; indeed the difficulty is so great that the task has seldom been attempted and not always with happy consequences. And yet I have felt that I could not fail of moderate success in this matter if I could reflect with any skill the enthusiasms of my own delight, since I believe that the fire of natural and spontaneous interest in one mind has the quality of producing a corresponding exaltation in another.

There are elements of mathematical thought which illuminate my spirit with a brilliant radiance whose after-images are pleasant to contemplate. Perhaps I can not bring to you now one of these moments of illumination of joy, for one can not produce them to order or easily recapture them but I can hope to present certain after-images which show some qualities of the original.

The impulse for the advancement of knowledge which is both most fundamental and most far-reaching in its practical and ideal effects is that which grows out of the pursuit of truth for truth's sake. What do we mean by this? What do we mean by mathematics for its own sake? It is clear that we do not intend to set up mathematics as a monster which must be worshipped, whom it is our duty to delight with the incense of human sacrifice. We mean rather to direct attention to the human values which are inherent in it apart from its use as a tool in any of the varied ways in which it may be so employed. Our purpose is to focus attention upon its primary values, those which it has in and of itself, those which are intimate to its own character and do not depend upon its uses outside of its own domain.

We are fundamentally so constituted that we delight in knowing for the sake of knowing. It is our most abstract and

* Reprinted from the *Scientific Monthly*, vol. 14, 1922, pp. 447–468. By permission of the Science Press.

our most general motive in science. It actuates most power-fully our choicest spirits, moving them sometimes with a fervor akin to that of religion. A marvelous curiosity to know, insatiable and always demanding further satisfactions, creates a longing which can be relieved only by knowledge. It projects itself into the unknown and leads the researcher in ways yet untrodden to a goal which can not be foreseen. At the outer boundary line of knowledge, faint glimmerings may be detected in the darkness of ignorance beyond. What beck-ons us forth we do not know. Whether it can bring us any good we have no means of foretelling. It may lead us to a tragical something which will make it necessary for us, in much pain, to cast away some of our most cherished preju-dices. But, whatever lies beyond in that which is concealed from our present vision,

> We work with this assurance clear,
> To cover up a truth for fear
>   Can never be the wisest way;
> By every power of thoughtful mind
> We strive a proper means to find
>   To bring it to the light of day.

Systematic and Unsystematic Thought

In its further reaches mathematics is perhaps the most ab-struse of our mental disciplines; but in its first stages it is the simplest of those sciences which have attained permanence of result. Mathematics is the field of thought in which perma-nent progress is easiest. It has obtained this facility through abstraction. The problems of nature are complex beyond our ability to cope with or perceive. In the first attempt to make progress in the way of definite conquest, we must abstract from the complexity of the situation and attain to a new one relatively much simpler. In fact we may find it necessary to create a new situation having certain analogies with the actual one of nature but being so much simpler that we are able to grasp far more successfully the interrelations of its parts. It is precisely this procedure which has guided the development of mathematics.

It is not that the mathematician refuses to be interested in the immeasurable complexity of nature. It is rather that he seeks permanence of conquest, even though it be at the ex-pense (in the first instance, at least) of a narrowed range of use. The way in which mathematics has interacted usefully with other elements in the progress of thought justifies her method of abstraction as profitable; it certainly conforms to the requirements of esthetic delight for the mathematician himself.

But the abstractions of mathematics leave us in a rarefied atmosphere too far removed from concrete experience to be a satisfactory resting-place for the mind of an inquisitive organism like man. He seeks to get closer to concrete phenomena. But, unless he is content to deal in vague and uncertain generalities, he finds the complexity of nature far too great for him even though he has forged a mathematical tool to assist in his labors. He must still confine attention to certain groups of phenomena abstracted from their surroundings. He must try, so to speak, to lift them from the matrix of their environment. Thus we arrive at the exact sciences of natural phenomena, as, for instance, the science of mechanics, through the use of abstraction as a necessary preliminary to exact and permanent intellectual conquest.

But it is clear that we do not understand even these restricted ranges of phenomena which we have separated in thought but not in reality from their environment until we have considered all the elements in that environment and have synthesized the disjoined knowledge of its parts into a comprehensive understanding of the whole. When we come to these questions of greater complexity we feel less certain of our results and far less confident of the permanence of our conclusions. The history of philosophy with its changing systems and the flux of its emphasis is a striking commentary on the difficulty of the general problem. And even here in the comprehensive problems of philosophy itself large abstraction has already been made from the complexity of phenomena and life and existence.

In definite contrast with the systematic thought of mathematics, the natural sciences, and certain parts at least of philosophical truth and speculation, stands the unsystematic thought of art and literature. Here one deals with the actual complexity of life and even with the character of individuals and their emotions. "It is the privilege of art to represent at a glance the whole of its object, and thus to produce at once a total effect on the mind of the beholder." Not infrequently men of science have seemed to overlook the importance of this body of unsystematic thought in art and especially in literature. But it appears that the development of unsystematic thought is necessary to sanity; not that its unsystematic character as such contributes to this end, but that through no efforts being made at systematic statement one can allow the whole flux of life to be reflected at once, at least so far as to have no purposed exclusions. If one is to have the systematic exactness of pure science it can be only after many relevant considerations are shorn off and attention is fixed on a part only (usually a small part) of the whole. This is necessary to definite conquest and the method is to be freely used. If one stops with this, however, a one-sided unbalanced view results which contributes forcibly to a lack of sanity in outlook and general judgment. With the continued development of systematic thought, let us encourage and support the free development of unsystematic thought in poetry and other forms of literature and art. The latter have abiding qualities of intrinsic human worth which science can never replace.

The domains of systematic and unsystematic thought have usually little effect the one upon the other; and yet between these two great arteries of our culture there must be somewhere a vital connection. The historians of general thought have not yet properly taken into account the vast body of unsystematic thought in the literatures of the world where for millenniums it has awaited their research. Nor on the other hand has the poetry of exact truth been written nor have its cultural elements in any representative case found their way into the general thought of mankind.

Literature not only takes the complex whole of life at a glance but it also internationalizes its local subjects and gives them a value which endures independently of time and place. Mathematics and poetry lie, if not on, at least not far from the extremes, the one of systematic and the other of unsystematic thought, and thus are about as far removed as possible one from the other. And yet they have a very striking common property, namely, the property of permanence. No other large domains of thought than mathematics and literature have acquired large bodies of truth retaining their values essentially unimpaired for two thousand years, not in a stagnant state, but in a state of vitality and effectiveness. It is a matter of great inspiration to see the Greek geometry and the Greek tragedy surviving through the ages and retaining the active power to excite our admiration and increase our happiness to-day.

The Language of Exact Truth

Communication to others requires the previous construction of a language having the requisite flexibility. If we look into the remote origins of our culture we shall find reason for believing that it was language which initiated the marvelous release of the powers of man inherent and undeveloped in our primitive ancestors and coming to their fruition only after many ages of progress. It was and is a fundamental element in accumulating and retaining the heritage of the past so that each new generation, in periods of development, is able to begin a little further on than the preceding one.

There is something subtle in the way in which language makes it possible to pass the experience and thought of one generation along to the next. The phenomena of nature present themselves to us ordered in space and time, but without apparent logical connections to bind them together. As long as we meet them merely in the multiplicity of their separate existences we can not get far towards an understanding of them or of a mastery over them. It is necessary that they shall be ordered into groups or sets, each held together by some tie which serves in our mind either as a unifying or as a connecting element. The combination of distinct elements into a whole and the formation of these groups depends on a process which the mind constructs for itself slowly and only after much labor. Any means of giving a considerable measure of permanence to the constructions of one individual mind or of one age, will be of great value in maintaining mastery and effecting its further development.

Let us conceive, if possible, the condition of prehistoric man at a time when language was in the process of construction for the first time. When a tribe of men reach agreement concerning the common elements of a set of objects, as for instance the trees of the forest, and signalize a realization of their common features by giving to them some such name as tree, they crystallize into definite form a class of experiences felt by each of them in a more or less vague way. The idea denoted by the word becomes more distinct by constant recurrence and both word and idea take their places as part of the mental possessions of man.

This primitive process has been repeated in all ages of our history; it recurs often in the present day, notably in connection with the development of scientific thought. In youth we listen to the words of those of the previous generation, trace in their features some mark of the anxieties through which they have lived, and share remotely their enthusiasms and aspirations, their passions and their joys. But we receive through them in the language which they teach us a more living inheritance and a more eloquent testimonial to their ways of thought. "Unknowingly they have themselves altered the tongue, the words and sentences, which they received, depositing in these altered words and modes of speech the spirit, the ideas, the thought of their lifetime. These words and modes of speech they handed down to us in our infancy, as the mould wherein to shape our minds, . . . as the instrument with which to convey our ideas. In their language, in the phrases and catchwords peculiar to them, we learnt to distinguish what was important and interesting from what was trivial or indifferent, the subjects which should occupy our thoughts, the aims we should follow, the principles and methods which we should make use of."

A word or a way of thought into which so much experience of the race has been instilled can easily be taught to the children of a new generation and be made to serve for them as a nucleus about which they can gather experiences of their own similar to those first embodied in the language. Thus through the various words which they use and the various turns of phrase which they employ they have a subtle means of assistance in organizing their early experience so that they are able to make much more rapid acquisition of knowledge than their ancestors who first had the confusion of unorganized impressions out of which to construct the initial organization of truth.

To the individual who is brought up in a civilized and intellectual age words and their organization into sentences certainly come earlier than clear and conscious thought. Through the use of our parents' tongue we are introduced to the complex processes of highly abstract reasoning in a manner which is truly marvelous. The way of thinking of our ancestors, preserved in some measure in the constructions of their language and in the peculiar ways of expressing thought developed through ages of progress, becomes to us our most precious heritage from the past. A highly significant part of the development of mankind is summarized into the forms and words of language in such a way as to be capable of transmission and to be of unmeasured value in passing on to the children the acquisitions of their ancestors.

What the language of daily life does for the thought of usual intercourse the language of mathematics does for the thought of exact truth. Everything which I have said about language in general I can now transfer to the language of mathematics in respect to its use in connection with exact thought. It furnishes the essential means for the expression of the latter. It supplies the support without which the mind would be unable to carry through the processes necessary to attain the more profound or far-reaching results. There is a certain storing, as it were, of intellectual force in the mathematical symbols from which it can be released suddenly with almost explosive power. These become mighty engines through the aid of which we can rear intellectual structures quite inaccessible to our unsupported power.

The invention of number was the first step in the creation of the language of mathematics; and the choice of adequate and convenient symbols for the representation of integers is one of the chief triumphs of the intellect. A long and arduous mental struggle, in which some of the finest minds of antiquity had part, preceded the conception of zero and the introduction of a symbol to represent it in the way now familiar even to our children. The result of a long and important development of thought is embodied compactly in this remarkable sign. The introduction of a symbol like 4/5 marks a new stage in the development of mathematics. The general fact is repeated in many situations; but I can not go into a further analysis of this matter. It is sufficient to our purpose if we realize that the language of mathematics is an essential support to the mind in all its processes of exact thought and that the results emerging in this way can be expressed only in mathematical terms.

Being a lover both of mathematics and of poetry I enjoy finding certain general similarities between them. I have already alluded to one very striking common property of them, namely the property of permanence. I wish now to direct your attention to the historical fact that poetry was the primary and most important means by which the language of ordinary intercourse was brought to a stage of relative perfection just as mathematics was the essential means in creating the language of exact truth. Ordinary language having been brought to perfection by the labors of the poets was then appropriated by writers of prose; exact language having been developed by the mathematicians has been employed freely by the cultivators of every exact science.

Mathematics and Philosophy

Philosophy and mathematics started life together. After a brief period of companionship they parted company and each went its own way. Mathematics was the first science to emancipate itself from the tutelage of philosophy; it gained its freedom at the dawn of Greek civilization. Mechanics next succeeded towards the close of the Grecian period, physics obtained its independent position at the opening of the modern era, biology about the beginning of the nineteenth century, and psychology in its latter half. Sociology as an independent science has hardly yet passed its period of infancy.

When men began consciously to cast about them to understand their universe, they found it possible in a relatively short time to procure and contemplate a large body of unsystematic thought, a wealth of philosophic explanation, and a rather large body of speculative proto-science of nature. But in respect of mathematical knowledge they had to begin much nearer the bottom. In the less exact disciplines there was an ebb and flow of movement with a general progress forward, accompanied often by a discarding of what at one time was considered well established. But in mathematics a conquest once made is almost never lost and there is a consequent unbroken enlargement of doctrine. Since it pushes its conquests out in many directions, is frequently annexing new domains, never yields up what it has once attained, and remains youthful in its spirit of conquest, mathematics is destined to become, if indeed it is not already, the most extensive scientific doctrine in the whole range of knowledge.

Early in the history of thought philosophy soared the heights on wings of speculative grandeur and soon reached an eminence which it has never surpassed. Mathematics took time to dig deep till it was in possession of secure foundations on which to build. Here it reared a magnificent structure of enduring beauty. In our generation this mathematics has reached forth a hand of conquest and has annexed certain restricted domains of philosophy. "The first real advance in logic since the time of the Greeks was made independently by Peano and Frege—both mathematicians" working with the tools and from the point of view of mathematics. In former days the nature of infinity and continuity belonged to philosophy, but now it belongs to mathematics. An important part of the theory of classes has been annexed by this greedy conqueror.

But more than all this, it has injected its spirit into a large province of modern philosophy. Among the philosophies of the present day Bertrand Russell distinguishes three principal types, combined in varying proportions in single philosophers but in essence and tendency distinct, namely, the classical tradition, evolutionism, and the method of logical atomism. The last has crept into philosophy through the critical scrutiny of mathematics. According to Russell it represents "the same kind of advance as was introduced into physics by Galileo: the substitution of piecemeal, detailed, and verifiable results for large untested generalities recommended only by a certain appeal to the imagination."

A doctrine which lay quiescent in the domain of philosophy for many generations has recently been brought by mathematical methods into the activity of vigorous life. The modern theory of relativity is a precise physico-mathematical realization of the philosopher's speculation of relativity. The existence of the philosophical doctrine has been of profound value in the creation of the mathematical doctrine; but the latter is now so far in advance of the former that the philosopher is rare who is able to follow the train of thought by which the more exact theory is brought to fullness. This mathematical conquest of a domain of philosophy has in our generation yielded a penetrating insight into certain fundamental matters both of physics and of philosophy. A theory of gravitation, satisfying for the most part in its broad aspects, has come into being for the first time. Under the impulse of this theory our notions of force and mass have suffered considerable change and our conceptions of time and space have undergone a veritable revolution.

Without going into more detail in these matters, I may insist upon the fact that one of the profound intrinsic human worths of mathematics lies in its conquest over intellectual matters of perennial interest on which agreement cannot be reached until they are penetrated by the spirit and methods of mathematics and the invariant elements of truth are extracted and justified by a convincing array of precise evidence.

Mathematics and the Foundations of Science

Mathematics is autonomous. What is intimate to it, its nature and structure and laws of being, must be sought in itself. Logically the mathematical sciences can be developed in complete independence of all other sciences; and when pursued in this way to their goal they completely realize their object. Owing to its self-sufficiency, its abstract character, and its exclusion of complicating factors from the ideal considerations with which it is concerned, mathematics is essentially easier than the other branches of systematic truth. The appearance of greater difficulty, which has deceived most people, grows out of the fact that it is relatively further advanced than any other subject. It requires the learner longer in mathematics than in other sciences to attain an elevation from which he may enjoy the prospect of unexplored territory. Its wildernesses are further from the confines of civilization; and the ignorant picture them as filled with horrid monsters of indescribable physiognomy. But the hardy intellectual traveler who explores in this land of the far unknown finds nature gracious, there as well as here, in dispensing her beauties and joys and comforts.

As a discipline which is unique through its being more completely developed than any other it may be utilized as an object lesson of importance in the development of thought. The mind has not been able to chart unknown regions and to explore them systematically. Truth, when attained, often has an appearance quite unexpected. Its central characteristics can not be anticipated before it appears in thought. Consequently, the extended development of any discipline affords a means of analyzing the methods and foundations of successful thinking and of extracting by such analysis principles of guidance for all domains of exact thought. In certain important respects mathematics affords just such a support to the mind in finding its way to truth; it has continuously rendered a service of this character since the days of the early Greek philosophers. This contribution has varied in detail from age to age, ranging from marvelous uses in interpreting physical phenomena to marked support in speculative philosophy and the theory of knowledge.

During the last half century or so mathematics has come definitely to a stage of self-consciousness with respect to its processes and presuppositions; and these have been analyzed and subjected to critical logical scrutiny. The foundations on which the subject is built are understood with a completeness foreign to any other domain of thought. From this fact it may well serve as a matter of instruction to point the way to a suitable and needed analysis of the presuppositions on which any given discipline is founded.

The importance of such an analysis seems not always to be apprehended. The sciences of nature are shot through with presuppositions not recognized. Even in the more precise reasoning of mathematics there was much to be elucidated by a critical scrutiny; and certain presuppositions had to be brought into the focus of attention before it could be properly said that we understood the foundations of the science. Elsewhere such analysis has been made only very imperfectly; the success achieved by mathematics in this work has not yet borne its proper fruit. It has been made clear that no science has been brought to a truly objective stage in its development until the presuppositions lying back of it are perceived as such and the grounds for making them are clearly realized. In the sciences of nature this process is more difficult than in mathematics; this, indeed, accounts for the fact of earlier success in mathematics than elsewhere. But when the result is once achieved in one science no other should rest satisfied until the same end is reached in an appropriate way.

Mathematics and the Method of Thought

Perhaps it will be agreed that we can nowhere study the processes of thought, by which the intellect reaches appropriate decisions, more effectively than in that domain where it has been most successful in attaining enduring results of significant value. If this principle is agreed upon, it is a corollary that mathematics is a field of thought which will yield us some of our most definite information as to the essential elements in the methods of clear and accurate thinking. Unfortunately, mathematicians themselves have generally been but little interested in the broad principles of method which their achievements are capable of bringing to light; they have usually been disposed to stand apart from the broader questions of a theory of knowledge, satisfied apparently with the self-sufficiency of their own discipline. Outside of their fold there has never been a group of thinkers with the requisite information and training to elicit from the body of mathematics the instruction which it is thus capable of affording. This field of promising possibility lies uncultivated while we lack those advantages which its fruitage well may yield.

It is important to ascertain the character of these regions

of thought in which new methods have most frequently arisen into clear consciousness. Owing to precision of ideas and processes in mathematics we can answer that question definitely and with considerable confidence for that discipline. New methods have usually come to light in connection with well-defined and well-restricted problems. Experience has forced upon us a realization of the profound importance of deep penetration into even the simplest matters. When a new means of illuminating them has been discovered its radiance spreads to adjacent fields and often overlaps great barriers to shed new light in most unexpected places. The connections between different elements of thought can not be anticipated successfully; it requires the event to exhibit them. The presuppositions which underlie truth become apparent gradually, as we derive the remotest consequences of what is already known. For the researcher everywhere the character of the success in mathematics emphasizes the importance of detailed and penetrating and carefully analyzed investigations of basic matters.

The continuous advance in the understanding of the presuppositions of our science, the axioms or postulates on which it rests, and the resulting modifications in our views of its significance impress us constantly with the supreme necessity of the logical coherence of knowledge. No principle is thoroughly understood until all of its consequences are developed and their ramifications are ascertained. This process can be carried out only through the most searching logical scrutiny; it is desirable that the intuition shall be present in discovery, but the logical faculties should dominate exposition completely. "To supersede the employment of common reason, or to subject it to the rigor of technical forms, would be the last desire of one who knows the value of that intellectual toil and warfare which imparts to the mind an athletic vigor, and teaches it to contend with difficulties and to rely upon itself in emergencies." But when its results are once attained and they are to be put to the test of a systematic organization for determining the coherence and consistency of the parts, no glow should be permitted except that which comes from the cold light of logic.

A more deep-lying problem of the method of exact thought is brought out by the question as to the fundamental character of that mental process by which scientific truth is discovered. Natural science always proceeds in one of three ways: mathematically, experimentally, or by hypothesis. Have all these methods fundamental matters in common one with another and with the processes of mathematics itself? And, if so, are they of such sort that it is useful to the progress of science or to our delight in it to have them brought to attention? Owing again to the relatively more advanced state of mathematics as compared with the natural sciences we can consider for it, in a more objective way than for them, this question as to the basic characteristics of the process of discovery.

Not a few mathematicians are agreed that these characteristics are summed up in considerable measure in the word invention. Some of the things in mathematics one may think of as being discovered; but others, and the more fundamental things, seem to have been created by the mind. The positive integers, for instance, were not found in nature but were created by the human spirit. After their creation many of their properties have been discovered. This relation between invention and discovery pervades most of the mathematical literature. Mathematical space has been created, not found in nature, as is shown by the fact that the mathematician has several kinds of three-dimensional space as well as numerous spaces of higher dimensions. It is true that his creative power was released through observation of the environment; but it can not be maintained that the environment dictated the geometry since in that case only one geometry could have resulted. A full analysis of the matter would carry us much too far afield, but we may assert that the process of discovery in mathematics is primarily that of invention.

This leads the mathematician to suspect that the method of exact thought everywhere is largely dependent upon invention, that the hypotheses of science are not extracted from nature but are invented by the mind through a release of its powers brought about by natural phenomena. Since one's procedure in forming hypotheses is doubtless much affected by his conception of the nature of the process it is important that the laborers in each science shall ascertain the corresponding fundamental characteristics of their processes of discovery.

If we should suppose that the advance of knowledge among the most cultivated people is in the direction of making life not worth while this would operate to destroy the part of society so affected with pessimism and the whole earth would ultimately be left to the less advanced. Thus a philosophy which makes life not worth while will have a natural tendency to destroy itself, so that it can not become permanent. That philosophy of the method of thought which results from a contemplation of mathematical progress leads to a doctrine which dignifies the process of thinking, exalting it to a place of veritable creative grandeur. It proceeds in the direction of making life worth living. It is optimistic in outlook and thus has one of the first qualities which are essential to permanence.

The Invariants of Human Nature

Another value of mathematics is in its creation of clarification for its own use of various concepts which are afterward seen to serve as a unifying element about which other large domains of truth may be systematically organized and the relations of fact thus be brought to clearer understanding. Everywhere we are confronted by change; nature seems to be in an eternal flux. The complexity of particular phenomena is bewildering and we should be lost in their maze if we could not find some means of ascertaining the elements of permanence in the midst of the flux. In mathematics we have the same situation freed of distracting elements and idealized in a way which makes it possible to give a rather complete analysis of the whole matter. The flux and change of nature is replaced, in the ideal situations of mathematics, by what we call a group of transformations. The elements in consideration are subject to transformation according to the laws prescribed by the group which governs the phenomena; and our problem is to determine the things which are unchanged in the midst of the general flux allowed by the controlling group; in other words, we are seeking what we call the invariants, or the invariant combinations, of the elements subject to the flux permitted by the group. This conception, vaguely present in much of scientific speculation, has been recreated by mathematics into precise form, has been clarified, and has been utilized so fully that we now find it to be true that a large portion of the whole of mathematics has to do consciously or unconsciously with the theory of invariants. The essential elements of the logical characteristics of a situation of this sort are brought out clearly by the mathematical theory. The resulting body of truth furnishes us with a model by which we may be guided in the contemplation of the elements of permanence in any changing situation.

Whatever the subject of inquiry in any domain of exact thought there are certain entities whose mutual relations we desire to ascertain. The combinations which have an unalterable value under the changes to which the entities are subjected are their invariants. It is the purpose of the theory of invariants to determine these combinations, elucidate their properties, and express in terms of them the laws which are involved in the given situation. The "laws of nature" are expressions of invariant relations under the changes occurring in nature or brought about by directive agency. Two problems concerning natural phenomena demand attention. If we know the group of changes we may demand the determination of the invariants; if we know the invariants we may demand the determination of certain (if not all) possible groups under which these invariants persist. To enforce the judgment that invariants are a fundamental guide in present day science we have only to cite the fact that the theory of relativity has been developed in intimate dependence upon and under the guidance of the theory of invariants.

To pursue this matter further would carry us too far in the direction of a study of the usefulness of mathematics in the development of natural science, a matter which we are purposely excluding from present consideration. It has been said by them of old time that the proper study of mankind is man. Our purpose keeps us closer to this problem than to the study of nature. It is a fair question to ask what mathematics has to teach us concerning human nature. What do we mean by human nature except those characteristics of individual people which are unchanged from one to another, and from age to age? Those elements which are invariant through the whole group of human beings as far as they may be brought under observation? And how shall we determine the characteristics of this human nature other than by an analysis of the invariant elements in human experience and thought?

It can not be maintained that mathematics affords the best means for pursuing this study. In fact, it is probably generally supposed that mathematics makes no contribution at all to the problem of human nature, of the invariants among the qualities of individuals; we shall attempt to show that this judgment is incorrect.

The best means of studying human nature of course arises from the usual relations of life. But these in themselves are quite insufficient for a complete analysis. The continued acceptance of a large body of vital mathematical truth through some millenniums suggests the invariant character of certain elements of human thought in its logical aspects, just as the continued appeal of ancient poetry (for instance) to people of cultivated taste bespeaks an unchanging element of human nature in its finer emotional aspects. The presence of such invariant elements, wherever they may be found, is an instructive matter for the historian of culture and civilization.

Where can one find a systematic analysis of literature, that great storehouse of material for the understanding of human nature and the progress of unsystematic thought, having for one of its primary objects the ascertainment of the invariant elements of human nature in its emotional aspects? A study of the changes in taste and their cause contributes indirectly to this end; but both literature and mathematics, in different ways and with reference to difference parts of our nature, can be made to yield important values towards an understanding of its invariant elements.

Since the historian of thought and civilization is seeking to bring his analysis of the progress of culture into systematic form it is perhaps no great surprise that he has found it difficult, and so far has not found it possible, to utilize successfully the truth which is half-concealed and half-revealed in the unsystematic thought of literature. But it is rather astonishing that such historians of thought have not been able to utilize the systematic work of mathematics in their expositions. I know of only a single instance where a general analysis of the progress of thought has taken an adequate account of the domain of mathematics, and that is in the work of J. T. Merz on "The History of European Thought in the Nineteenth Century."[1] This excellent general analysis has not had for one of its purposes to bring out the invariant qualities of human thought, and hence of human nature, as they are made manifest by the abiding truths of mathematics. The contribution which mathematics has to make to the study of human nature has not yet been considered in a systematic way.

And still it is certain to those who contemplate the nature of mathematical truth that many characteristic qualities of human thought are to be determined from such an analysis. It is a significant fact for the understanding of ourselves that the demonstrations in Euclid's *Elements* gain the same adherence to-day as in his time and in all the intervening ages; an invariant quality in the processes of reasoning and the ground for conviction through demonstration abides through the ages. There is absolute agreement in all times and all places that the number of prime integers is infinite, bespeaking a unity of the whole race in its understanding of the properties of elements conceived in the first place with exactness. The properties of a Euclidean triangle are in harmonious agreement even though they have been discovered by numerous thinkers of many generations. A sphere did nothing for the Greeks contrary to what it does for us to-day. The properties of a cube are invariant, whoever derives them and in whatever age he lives. It is an eternal truth that every integer is the sum of squares of four integers, and there is unanimity as to this fact and as to its demonstration. The persistence of mathematical theorems and the continued agreement as to their proof indicates a profound unity in the characteristic thought processes of those who contemplate them, exhibiting one fundamental phase of human nature.

Artistic Delight in Mathematical Truth

Truth serves many ends. When a science has reached a certain stage of development, varying greatly with the character of its material, it begins to throw off into the body of society great practical or even esthetic values which could not be realized without it. Astronomy has enabled us to have some conception of the vastness of space and the hugeness of the mass of matter, perhaps infinite in its totality, distributed through this space. Geology has released the imagination to contemplate enormous periods of time and, through its influence on biology, has rendered marked service in making possible our conception of the long progress of life on the planet, culminating in man. Mathematics, by exhibiting a body of truth which can live through millenniums without needed corrections, and at the same time can grow in magnitude and range and interest, has given the human spirit new ground for believing in itself and for rejoicing in its power of consistent thought.

It is not enough to accumulate the elements of knowledge or even by means of them to control nature for our use; we must appropriate them by idealizing them into things of beauty and motives to conduct. Truth may be made to yield the highest delights of contemplation in the spirit of artistic performance. This is generally realized in the case of the unsystematic truth afforded by literature and the other fine arts. It is less in evidence in the greater body of systematic truth. But when the latter is brought to its highest order of perfection, as it is in the domain of mathematics, it becomes capable of yielding the purest and most intense delights in artistic excellence. They are of a sort to be enjoyed in large measure only after an adequate training; and in that respect there is a certain exclusiveness about them. But to those who are willing to pay the price of adequate knowledge mathematics yields a gratification of the artistic sense surpassed by that arising from no other source. "The musician plays and the artist paints simply for the pure love of creation." The mathematician creates abstract and ideal truth for the pure love of discovery and of contemplation of the beauty of his mental handiwork.

In pursuing esthetic satisfactions we create a beautiful theory for the sake of our delight in it, as in the case of the theory of numbers or of abstract groups. Working in such fields with the simpler elements of mathematical thought we make progress of a sort not at first possible with the more complex materials. We bring the theory to a higher state of perfection; there are fewer lacunæ; the connections of the various parts are exhibited with clarity; we have a sense of having seen to the root of the matter and having understood it in its basic characteristics. The theory thus developed becomes an ideal in the light of which we get a new conception of what should be attained in other fields where the labor and the difficulty are greater. Results in one field of mathematics may thus become of great value in a totally different range of mathematical ideas or even in other disciplines altogether. Moreover, when such progress is attained we often find that the tools employed in bringing it about are sufficient for dealing with more difficult matters, so that the one completed theory furnishes us not only the ideal, but also the means, for further valuable progress.

A characteristic delight in mathematical truth is that which arises from economy of thought realized through the creation of general theories. When we develop the consequences of a set of broad hypotheses we find that our results, which are attained by a single effort, have applications at once in many directions. Thus we see the common elements of diverse matters and are able to contemplate them as parts of a single general theory pleasing for its elegance and comprehensiveness.

Fundamentally mathematics is a free science. The range of its possible topics appears to be unlimited; and the choice from these of those actually to be studied depends solely on considerations of interest and beauty. It is true that interest has often been, and is to-day as much as ever, prompted in a considerable measure by the problems actually arising in natural science, and to the latter mathematics owes a debt to be paid only by essential contributions to the interpretation of phenomena. But, after all, the fundamental motive to its activity is in itself and must remain there if its progress is to continue.

"The desire for the one just form which always inspires the literary artist visits most men sometimes" and is ever present to the mathematician in his hours of creative activity. The one just form which the mathematician seeks is more ideal and perhaps more delightfully artistic than that sought by any other thinker; for it is primarily a form of abstract thought in which he is interested, a form which remains the same as ages come and go, as languages are developed and die away, as the canvas of the painter rots to fragments and the material of the sculptured image is resolved by decomposition into its elemental dust. It is a thing of beauty which is indeed a joy forever.

For many people the numerous practical applications of mathematics have obscured its artistic elegance. But it is not the only fine art which in another aspect is also of the greatest practical utility. This quality it shares with the noble art of architecture. The two equally satisfy the following informal definition given by Sidney Colvin: "The fine arts are those among the arts of man which spring from his impulse to do or make certain things in certain ways for the sake, first, of a special kind of pleasure, independent of direct utility, which it gives him so to do or make them, and next for the sake of the kindred pleasure which he derives from witnessing or contemplating them when they are so done or made by others." Both mathematics and architecture possess all the qualities here enumerated. Each is of essential practical utility, contributing necessary elements to the material comforts of man. And, more than this, each delights the artistic sense through beauties peculiar to itself and furnishing the ideal reason for its existence.

From a certain point of view the four main divisions of thought—mathematics, natural science, philosophy, that unnamed one ruling without definite system in the domain of art and literature—are the stones and brick and mortar from which is builded the culture of the time, into which are wrought the values received from the past, and through which our development shall proceed to the acquisition of new power for further conquest. We break the environment into parts in thought and from these we fashion new objects such as never before existed in the universe—objects both concrete and ideal—and these we put together in ways well pleasing to ourselves to serve the ends we propose or erect the constructs we conceive.

But this is too mechanical to be the whole truth. The more profound values lie deeper and have their fruition only in the fullness of the character of man. If science did not touch a more profound matter than mere motion or reach to constructs which can not be adequately pictured by material symbols, it would fall far short of the glory of Living Thought. But it does forcibly react in a profound way with all our activities, particularly through the emotions excited by the play of the artistic sense. In fact, the elements of all Thought are parts of one body, living and organized, inspired by the breath of the Universe itself and pulsating with the life of truth in its deeper manifestations.

The Problem of Consistent Thinking

The leading characteristic of man is the power to think. There is nothing of higher esthetic interest than to determine whether we can think consistently. This fundamental question can be answered in the affirmative only by exhibiting the results of consistent thinking. The existence of mathematics affords the best conceivable proof of its possibility and gives the spirit of man leave to believe in itself, since here admittedly is a body of consistent thought maintaining itself for generations and even for millenniums, able to sustain all the attacks of logic and all the tests of the practical life.

There was a time when this confidence in the permanence and consistency of mathematics was absolute. The fundamental methods of argumentation men conceived to belong to a class of innate or inherent ideas which had been put in the mind of man by the Creator. The initial hypotheses and basic notions of a mathematical discipline they thought of as belonging to the same category. If these innate ideas did not have all the elements of absolute certainty, there could be only one conclusion: the Creator had deliberately deceived man. Since they considered this to be absolutely impossible, they had complete confidence in the certainty of mathematical results.

Nowadays we seek a more earthly reason for confidence in our constructions in science. Our agreement that mathematics is possible as a consistent body of truth we now understand to rest on postulates for which admittedly we have no logical demonstration. Perhaps these postulates may be framed in the following way: Reasoning is possible and does not lead to wrong results when employed according to the universally accepted rules; mathematical objects can be created or discovered by the mind; we can actually formulate consistent axioms or postulates concerning these objects. With each of these three statements there are grave logical difficulties. We can not assert that we have an immediate perception of them as true; we can not, by direct illumination, see their validity. We must examine each of them in the cold light of experience and accept it only in so far as it meets the most exacting demands. Our confidence can never be absolute. As J. B. Shaw has said in his *Philosophy of Mathematics*: "We may found our deductions on what premises we please, use whatever rules of logic we fancy, and can only know that we have played a fruitless game when the whole system collapses—and there is no certainty that any system will not some day collapse!"

Let us proceed further with the difficulties of the situation. In all preceding generations conceptions in mathematics have been used with confidence which, in the experience of a later day, were found to be not sufficiently well defined: they have been discarded or essentially modified, sometimes after generations of confident use. It is not likely that men have heretofore always made mistakes of this kind and that we have suddenly come upon an age in which mathematical conceptions are refined to the last point of analysis.

We are then forced to the conclusion, however unwelcome it may be, that the certainty of mathematics after all is not absolute, but relative. To be sure, it is the most profound certainty which the mind has been able to achieve in any of its processes; but it is not absolute. The mathematician starts from exact data; he reasons by methods which have never been known to lead to error; and his conclusions are necessary in the sense, and only in the sense, that no one now living can point to a flaw in the processes by which he has derived them.

Let us make as concrete as possible the difficulties and the immense values which are at stake. Let us suppose that the Euclidian geometry should become untenable under the weight of constant accretions and should go crashing down to helpless ruin; in that day man's hope of reaching tolerable certainty anywhere in his thinking would be destroyed and even the world of mind would become a dark confusion of irrational elements. The character of such a loss suggests the magnitude of the present value.

What certainty have we that such loss does not impend? We have no logical demonstration of its impossibility; and in the nature of things can not have such a demonstration. The same uncertainty attends all other truth, and in even more marked degree. There is no logical certainty of the consistency or the permanence of truth; at most there is a moral certainty. From mathematics we have the strongest grounds for the latter. When thousands of persons through thousands of years examine thousands of theorems proved by numerous methods and in numerous connections and there is always absolute unanimity in the compelling character of the demonstration and the consistency of results, we have a ground of moral confidence so great that we can dispense with the proof of logical certainty and comfortably lay out our lives on the hypothesis of the permanence, consistency and accuracy of mathematical truth. The existence of mathematics gives the mind the best reason yet advanced for believing in its powers and the essential accuracy of its careful processes.

Emotional Exaltation Arising from the Contemplation of Mathematical Truth

A profound emotional exultation arises from the contemplation of mathematical truth either in the static aspect of accomplished results or in the dynamic aspect of a science with an everlasting urge to further development. By the ideal values which it constructs and by the permanence of its results mathematics gives to the spirit of man the right and the courage to believe in itself and to trust its controlled flights. Here it justifies its claims to preeminence more completely and more profoundly than in any other part of its broad domain. It exhibits a body of truth which is permanently pleasing and which exacts confidence at all times and among all thinkers who examine it.

By building first on its narrow and exactly conceived foundation and by adding bit by bit to its possessions of permanent truth, mathematics has made possible a release of the imagination of man such as can be completely realized to-day by only a relatively few individuals, a release however which will allow an expanse of the general human mind to-morrow or the next day. Vast new domains of contemplation are opened up by the non-Euclidean geometries, theories of hyperspace and space of an infinite number of dimensions, functions of an infinite number of variables and functions of lines. Such conquests give a new sense of power and mastery and increase the dignity of man. In the presence of so many beautiful creations of his thought "the mathematician lives long and lives young; the wings of his soul do not early drop off"; he rejoices in the grandeur of the heights to which his controlled imagination attains.

If one is to realize the intenser delights afforded by the contemplation of mathematics he must of course be a deep student of its secrets. It is only when he is able to devote a large share of his energy to research and is successful in the creation or discovery of important new truth that he may rejoice in the fullest glow of delight through a realization of himself in such ideal conquests. However important the work of preserving past discoveries and handing down to the future the accumulated tradition and however far-reaching such a stream of influence flowing in hidden ways in the minds of cultivated people, it can not be placed in the same category with that creative work which guides instructor and student alike and teaches generations what to think. It is the great glory of mathematics in our time that its achievements are being immensely enriched and extended by the researches of the present; so that this, the oldest of the sciences, has the vigor and the spring and the growth of the youngest of them. He who discovers a fact or makes known a new law or adds a novel beauty to truth in any way makes every one of us his debtor. How beautiful upon the highway are the feet of him who comes bringing in his hands the gift of a new truth to mankind!

Alone before the wild and restless force
Of nature we have seen man's active soul
Stand forth in awe without a sure resource
Of power to overcome or to control
The salient things submerged beneath the whole.
And we have seen in vision some new power
Spring up from hidden depths of mind and roll
With bounding joy to conquest, hour by hour
Increasing till the strength of man reached fullest flower.

What stage of progress have we now attained
In this process of far-unfolding thought?
What ground to think that it shall be maintained?
Have we the fullness of our conquest brought
And reached the depths where nature works and caught
From her the deepest blessing she can yield?
Or fathomed her profounder secrets fraught
With good, no major truth remaining sealed
From sight, with only minor things to be revealed?

If so, no glow of zeal could move our thought;
Our life would lose its meaning and its zest;
No vision of the future could be caught
By mind's prophetic penetration, blest
With prospect large; in pessimistic rest
And deep stagnation then must mind abide
Without a great compelling interest
To bring its power to action and to guide
Its strength to ways of joy or largest use provide.

But crescent science such a view as this
Dispels; for largest things with keen insight
We feel; the growth of knowledge must dismiss
From thought such pessimism; its darkening blight
Of shadow is illumed by sure foresight.
We joy to see new worth to be attained
And know the present conquest is but slight
Compared with wider truth that shall be gained
For thought's dominions, now by science unexplained.

We need the willing mind to consecrate
Its strength to finding truth, the zeal to bring
From nature's storehouse values good and great

And lay them at the feet of man. To wring
From restive nature some unwilling thing
Were joy supreme. The means for our release
To greater power we seek. The bounding spring
To growth shall move in us and never cease
To bring to us new joy and truth's renowned increase.

NOTES

[1] To this magistral work and to many articles in the *Encyclopædia Britannica* I am under deep obligations in connection with this address. I have also profited by reading C. J. Keyser's *The Human Worth of Rigorous Thinking*, Columbia University Press, 1916.

MATHEMATICS—THE SUBTLE FINE ART

James Byrnie Shaw

According to James Byrnie Shaw, the mathematician is a creator of beauty who works primarily with ideas as his medium. One of the fundamental characteristics of beauty is order. The basis of all mathematics is order; the universe is ordered rhythm. In mathematics are to be found many exquisitely beautiful theorems and relationships—creations of the highest artistic quality—produced by the great artists of mathematics. Even as the artist creates beauty for its own sake, so the mathematician is generally indifferent to the "utilitarian" value that his creations may or may not have.

Also from Professor Shaw's facile pen, scattered in various journals, may be found essays on "the aesthetics of the quadratic equation," "occult symmetry," "orders in imaginaries," "the unity of mathematics," "the hidden symmetries of mathematical groups," "mystic harmony," "shadow-orders," "rhythms in irrationals," and "kaleidoscopic rhythms." The distinctive quality of these essays is due to the happy combination of a rare gift of poetic expression, unusual insight into the subtle qualities of mathematics, and an intimate familiarity with the major fine arts not ordinarily vouchsafed to any one man.

Mathematics—The Subtle Fine Art*

I. Introduction

MATHEMATICIANS are often confronted with the question: "What is mathematics?" And a second follows in its train: "Why should mathematics be of interest to any but the few?" Many definitions of mathematics have been given, but upon examination they have all turned out to be inadequate. A good many thinkers have given answers to the second question, but they have never been very convincing. It has been urged that mathematics is useful. So it is, and to many its sole reason for being is the same as that of the kitchen scullion. Some one must do the drudgery. It has been urged that mathematics is the most powerful aid to logical or correct thinking. And it is true that mathematics seems at least to be correct. And mathematics never loses its creations. One can take considerable pleasure in the fact that one of my students expressed himself thus: "I am heartily thankful there is one subject in my curriculum that remains the same to-day as yesterday." When one thinks about it he sees that in all the range of human thought, but one subject has steadily added to its riches, and never has thrown away anything —mathematics. Science denies this decade what it taught last decade. History is questioned on every side. The sciences of humanity are ever remade. With the exception of mathematics all knowledge is subject to revision. This is an excellent reason for becoming acquainted with it, but it is not a necessary reason. For we meet a new question: Is mathematics knowledge, and if so, knowledge of what? This reduces the second question to the first, and we must consider it before we can consider the other. What is mathematics?

In order to arrive at an answer we must go back, as Descartes did, to the human consciousness itself. What do we find in the conscious life of man as the dominant essences

* Reprinted from the *Scientific Monthly*, vol. 39, 1934, pp. 420–433. By permission of the Science Press.

of that life? One is the ability to hoard the conscious life, to capture some of the wild birds that flit past our present. Another is the ability to wave a magic wand like Prospero and bring into being birds and butterflies, Ariel and all the trains of fairies, castles and storied towers, music and poetry. Man is a dreamer, but some of his dreams he can capture and keep.

These two characters have been evident at all times in the long stretch of the human race from the dawn of history to the present. Man has never accepted the world around him as do the animals. He has always undertaken to change it and make it into something different. He makes water run uphill; he piles up stone or steel even to the clouds; he tames the wild beast and puts him to work; he talks 'round the world; he protects himself so that he lives in the tropics or at the poles. Sometimes he is whirled about in the winds of nature, but he does not accept this fate. He remembers what he has done in the past and wherein he failed, and on the basis of these memories, which he calls knowledge, he conceives visions of what he can do in the future. He is constantly endeavoring to let loose an innate power, a desire for activity. It is not necessarily practical work he is doing, for just as often it is the exercise of the play desires he possesses. He often undertakes projects that have no particularly practical end. The dance for the green corn is to cause good crops, but it is also the outlet of spiritual power. What practical end does "The Tempest" serve? The modern slender spire that rises up in the heart of a swarming city is practical, perhaps, but it is far more the satisfying success of an artist to realize a dream. Man knows that he is not a mere spectator in the universe of phenomena, seeing things only by "flashes of lightning, all the rest darkness." Neither is he a walking doll, that says "mamma," then goes to the ashbarrel when broken. He is an adventurer, often undertaking the impossible, and making it possible. He is the living volcano of flame and dust which must release its power.

But his life is not simply the exhibition of activity. There is inside him, not always consciously, a longing which haunts him, a longing for an invisible, intangible, inaudible reality called beauty. This he finds is just as insistent as the desire for comfort. He must build a habitation for shelter, but he does more than this, for he builds it in such a way as to satisfy this desire for an elusive thing which later he calls beauty. In time this indeed comes to be more important than anything else, for he sees that this reality indeed is himself. It is a glorified expression of that which he sees himself potentially to be. Whatever means he may make use of will be as inadequate as are paper and ink to carry the impassioned lover's rhapsody. When the first primitive tribe with sweating labor managed to stand on end a huge monolith, their expression of the majesty and power of their first vague intuition of the Unknown, their own dim consciousness of capabilities, of powers to be attained only in the tedious march of centuries, reaching up higher than they, solid and undisturbed by rain or frost, was there nothing real and permanent for which this clumsy symbol stood? Even the archeologists and ethnologists who see in it nothing but a phallic symbol have to admit that the insurgency of life and the urge to creation are worth a symbol which shows them as eternal realities.

The twofold character of the psyche is easily evident with only a small amount of reflection and very little insight. There is the ability to crystallize the evanescent and flowing waves of events into definite and stable forms, and this is called knowledge. Then there is the constant urge to create new elements, more spontaneity, unguessed and undreamed forms of the inner life, and this is called art. So fleeting is the configuration of the psyche that the fixed and stable elements are ascribed not to it but to an objective world which is assumed to be independent of the psyche. Knowledge is assumed to be an understanding of an extraneous entity. Art is assumed to be mere play of the spirit, fleeting emotion, of only passing interest. Both assumptions are incorrect, since knowledge is the more or less temporary system of invariants the psyche plays with, while art is the emergence of the new life-forms of the psyche itself. Those creations of the psyche which it retains for awhile constitute knowledge, and the creating of a new form is art. It is easy to restate knowledge, since its forms are for awhile permanent, but to state art one must accompany the wild duck in its flight, must freeze the rainbow the sun produces against the shower of events. This means of course that knowledge and art are human, even though they plumb the absolute. What sort of psychical material a Martian cherishes as knowledge we can not know. What sort of art he creates we can not know either.

The stable routes from one item of knowledge to another we call logic. They seem to us to be necessary, but merely because we have made them habitual in going from one judgment to another. To find other routes would be an act of creation, which would be art, not logic, and this process of making new logic is actually going on. Stable modes of art would be impossible, since creation implies the unexpected, the versatile, the ever-new. This does not mean that in the creative process there is not a permanent reality. Reality does not mean fixity, crystalline structure. Any organism that maintains its individuality as an organism, even though subject to a steady flux of material, even though every atom, material or mental, is changing momentarily into a new atom, is still a reality. The human body is a reality, the immaterial sieve through which chemicals flow. The reality of art has this nature. An easy example is dual symmetry, the complementary phases together constituting the unitary symmetry. This may be in positive and negative number, geometric reflection in a plane mirror, in sine and cosine, in wave and particle, in the façade of a temple, in the right and left of the human form, in the purple and yellow of the sunset, in the assonance and dissonance in music, in the earthly and the heavenly love, in male and female, in good and evil —what matter the medium in which the dual symmetry express itself? The reality is that which generates the symmetry, the forms are adventitious. The stable idea of symmetry is knowledge, the actualizing of symmetry in some form is art. Indeed, knowledge and art are phases of a dual symmetry in the psyche itself, though there may also be found trinities, quaternities and an unlimited variety of other forms. The struggle of the poise of the spirit with its medium of expression is often intense: "White, white blossom, fall of the shattered cups day on day."[1] To many of the realities of art there do not correspond ideas; they are not expressible in the abstractions and static forms of language. The nearest approach in language is in creative, metaphorical, suggestive poetry. Hence stating an example in words is very inadequate, it is at best only a sort of ticket for reality itself. "Art is the very flowering, the tangible flowering, of the creative soul come to ecstasy."[2]

There is a constant interplay of the two characters of the psyche. It is the creative character which furnishes knowledge its hypotheses, the most steady source of advance in science. It is the crystallizing character which furnishes art its types of expression, the most steady source of production of art works. Research goes on all the time both ways. On the knowledge side it usually consists in an increase in dispersive power so as to split principles into more universal principles or more fundamental hypotheses. On the art side it usually consists in experiments made to find a more adequate method of handling the medium, so as to express the artist's vision. Often the apparently unrelated researches are the same down in the depths of the psyche. It has been pointed out that much of modern art is an actualizing in art forms of the same universal invariants as appear in science in the Einstein theory. Human life, after all, is unitary, and we should expect this symmetric dualism in its manifestations. When the crystallizations made by the psyche no longer are useful and do not fit our evolving experience, we have an advance in science. It sweeps away what was called knowledge, and puts it into the museum of discarded theories. Where is to-day the ether which fifty years ago had a density, a rigidity, an elasticity, and was indeed a collection of very contradictory qualities? When the forms used by the artist no longer convey his message, have become lifeless and unsuggestive, we have an advance in art. The daring imagination of Wagner in music gave a new meaning to musical forms. The multitude usually does not welcome these advances, for the multitude likes what it is in the habit of having, it resists change, and society in general is conservative. No doubt the first savage to use fire for cooking was accused of impiety, of trying to upset society, of increasing the difficulty of living.

The aspirations of the spirit, however, produce new events in art, and the study of such aspirations is in the end more important than the study of phenomena in the world of nature. Every aspiration has something which may be clasped to the heart and in this way become knowledge, knowledge of life and what it means. When these aspirations which find expression in art forms become organized into living forms, they become visions. These visions have been the dominating forces in the life of man through all the ages, much more than his material environment. Knowledge enables us to secure ourselves against the play of material powers that would destroy us, the frost, the lightning, hunger, pain, illness. But spiritual visions enable us to wish to be secure so that we may expand into flowers that will not perish under the hurricanes and tempests of nature. For a few decades, the study of material phenomena has occupied man extensively, science has become quite powerful, and its success in giving us power to control the world of nature makes it a dominating force in life. But when it undertook to explain the life of art and the spirit, its words were ashes in the mouth, and to-day its finality has vanished.

In his "Dance of Life," Havelock Ellis says: ". . . where we reach the sphere of mathematics, we are among the processes which seem to some the most inhuman of all human activities and the most remote from poetry. Yet it is here that the artist has the fullest scope for his imagination. . . . We are in the imaginative sphere of art, and the mathematician is engaged in a work of creation which resembles music in its orderliness, and is yet reproducing on another plane the order of the universe and so becoming as it were a music of the spheres. . . . The mathematician has reached the highest rung of the ladder of human thought. But it is always the same ladder which we have all of us been ascending, alike from the infancy of the individual, and the infancy of the race. Molière's Jourdain had been speaking prose for more than forty years without knowing it. Mankind has been thinking poetry throughout its long career and remained equally ignorant."

Many mathematicians have said that mathematics is art. Poincaré, Sylvester, Pringsheim, Kummer, Kronecker, Helmholtz, Bôcher, B. Peirce, Russell, Hobson, Picard, Hadamard, and many others, have felt and seen the qualities that beauty shows in the various parts of mathematics. And we may reverse the statement, and just as physics, which was an observational science, ultimately became "the theory of certain differential equations," and at present may be said to have become "the theory of certain linear operators," so art in every line, every phase, every mode of expression, has become the outward expression of certain forms of beauty, simply as sheer beauty. Pure art is as abstract as mathematics. No intention exists of representing nature or man, even in a glorified state. Debussy's nocturnes express sparkling flashes of spiritual insights, Picasso's diagrammatic paintings express designs of the spirit itself. Even if the attempt be futile, as John Gould Fletcher says, the artist must keep on:

> Like spraying rockets
> My peonies shower
> Their glories on the night.
> Towards the impossible,
> Towards the inaccessible,
> Towards the ultimate,
> Towards the silence,
> Towards the eternal,
> These blossoms go.

II. Mathematics

What any art undertakes to do is to give an expression to beauty. In the artist are living, evolving qualities which embody themselves in the art form. The art form once produced becomes part of human consciousness, and on the one hand incites the individual to become a creator himself, at least in a vicarious way, and on the other hand gives him something permanent which he can add to the stable organism he calls himself. At present we will pass over the first phase because we are interested in the second. As knowledge we examine the art form to discover what its structure is. For it has a definite structure, as has everything in the universe. Even if the art form is existent only as music, which passes away with the playing, or as the dance, which ceases when the dancer is still, there is involved in the whole event a definite structure. The static arts—architecture, painting, sculpture, poetry, mathematics—leave a permanent product which may be examined again and again, and the structure can be studied leisurely. But the dynamic arts are birds that must be studied on the wing. They are flowers whose petals expand with the seeing, and then they are gone. Even if they can be repeated, the new expression is never quite the same as the old. Yet they have a structure which is the same. The elements of structure as knowledge in beauty have been named: Rhythm, order, design, harmony. These appear in every art. In the distant future we may expect to find new elements of structure besides these. Of course to be an organism each work of art exhibits these elements as held together in unity. It must be sufficient unto itself. The "Unfinished Symphony" haunts us with wistfulness. In every case the artist brings into being a new creature for the world of spirit; he gives life to it; he watches it enter into his own being, and he may find that it helps him to interpret the riddle of the Sphinx. If we had time we could show that many new concepts of science have had an origin like this.

When we come to consider mathematics we may paraphrase Sandburg and say, "Mathematics is the achievement of the synthesis of hyacinths and biscuits." And we shall find the mathematician more interested in the hyacinths than in the biscuits. Mathematics is engaged in fact in the profound study of and the expression of beauty. The medium used is very ethereal, being pure ideas, nothing material, and this justifies the statement that mathematics is the subtle fine art. Its medium is sublimated to the very limit. It does not depend upon the perceptions of the senses, nor upon matter. No material experiment could have the slightest effect upon a mathematical theorem. The existence of its objects is not in the world of sight. Nature never makes a perfect circle, nor draws a straight line. No fractional numbers exist in her building material, nor is there such a thing as a negative. Kempe defined mathematics as the science of pure form, but this is a somewhat empty concept. C. S. Peirce defined it as the study of ideal constructions. But an ideal construction is a structure. And of what? And by ideal he did not mean abstract, ghostly, purely non-existent.

If now we examine the various parts of mathematics to see what they are essentially, we shall find that they are concerned with the study of these elements of beauty named above; perhaps with particular expressions of the elements, or in the most profound way with the very essence, the spirit of the element in any particular form. In each case there are two phases, one static, furnishing patterns for the element, the other dynamic, furnishing motricities for the element. A pattern is something that remains crystallized, a motricity is something that parades its life before us. The White Knight said to Alice, "That is not the song, it is the name of the song." Nor is the printed verse the song. The song is gone with the singing. Yet the singing has a flowing pattern which is a motricity. So we have patterns and motricities of rhythm, patterns and motricities of order, patterns and motricities of design, patterns and motricities of harmony. These we find are what mathematics is concerned about.

III. Rhythm

Rhythm is an element of the structure of beauty. But modern physics says that rhythm is the fundamental element in the structure of the entire material universe. It swings around in great spirals the hosts of some island universe distant 300,000,000 light years; it wheels the members of a solar system in their ponderous orbits; it turns the hugest planet like a flywheel; it pulses in the flow of photons of light; it is the heartbeat of the atom; it is the only element of structure known for matter and energy. Wave-mechanics is a new term, but it has become the basic study for the physicist.

When the dawn of intelligence made Eoandros notice the world he was in, he must certainly have soon become aware of the pound, pound, pound, of his overtaxed heart when he had fled the saber-toothed tiger. He must have noticed the rhythm in the beat of the waves on the shore of the lake. He heard rhythm in the call of the crow. Day and night was a persistent rhythm. The flowing curves of birds in their flight, the arrangement of the leaves on the stem of the daisy, the way the petals of the primrose grew, almost all the items of his daily life surrounded him with rhythms. As he developed he began to hold on to certain of these rhythms, and these became knowledge, the knowledge of numbers—at first integers, one, two, three, four, five. In trying to follow the differences in phyllotaxis on a stem he would find fractions, two in five, three in eight. He was beginning the theory of numbers, even though he did not know it. Theory of numbers is still the many-threaded web of mathematics, and is far from being fully untangled. But in essence it is only the study of the structure of pure rhythms. Each prime number starts a new series of ripples, and the list of primes has no end. Do all these waves exist in nature? Apparently not. The imagination of man far outruns the needs of nature. Even the numerous waves of the terrestrial ninety-two atoms occur only in very definite series. These series are quite few compared to the endless list there may be. It was indeed a great source of satisfaction to the physicist when he found out that the series were few in number. His multitudinous chaos is overwhelming enough, even at that. And even when the waves run in packets and simulate particles, the wave-crests furnish only a few rhythms.

Centuries later in the history of man a majestic figure down by the Icarian Sea draws diagrams in the sand. They have all the mystic properties of rhythm: triangles, squares, pentagons, pentagrams, hexagons, figures inscribed inside of figures; then tetrahedra, cubes, dodecahedra, the ikosahedron —even the names are still Greek—all were full of rhythm, and they gave Pythagoras a vision far ahead of his time, a vision of the whole universe as built on rhythm. Number ruled everything, he was quite convinced. And he was more nearly right than was thought until recently. But one dreary day he and his school were appalled to find that there was no rational rhythm between the side of a square and its diagonal. Irrational numbers had emerged and they frightened their creators, and their magnificent temple of rhythm tumbled in ruins around the little band. Little they dreamed of the innumerable arrays of irrational numbers yet to come, bringing intricate new rhythms. The years rolled on in their cycles, and then one day a rebellious youth named Évariste Galois looked more closely at the irrational roots of equations, and saw rhythm emerging again in beautiful new types. All algebraic irrationals come from certain normal equations, and each normal equation furnishes a flower whose petals are the roots, arranged in cycles and clusters of cycles, of two, three, four, five and so on. The simple flowers of Eoandros have expanded into complicated forms, but with very definite structure for their rhythms. The refractory quintic has been shown to depend on a normal equation of order sixty, but the sixty petals of this flower are arranged in fives, threes and twos, twelve fives, twenty threes, thirty twos, and the transition from one five to another is given by a dance pattern of great beauty. Hamilton playfully embodied it in his Icosian game, its first expression. Irrationals are a creation of the spirit of man, and show forth certain innate rhythms in his own spirit.

But rhythm is not confined to number. For we find that algebraic forms also have their rhythms, and the modular study of these—quite complicated in itself—consists in the finding of these rhythmic relations. An example is the field of symmetric expressions on N letters. Finite geometries also exhibit the same essence. Even in the study of linear differential equations we again discover systems of related functions much like the conjugate irrationals of Galois, for the Vessiot theory is just this in its study of the domain of functions which are roots of these differential equations.

More has emerged, too, than the static arrangements of frozen flowers. For Galois saw that the transitions from one of his sets to another were rhythmic also, and in the place of crystallized patterns we now have flowering motricities. He called them groups in connection with the roots of equations. And these groups, too, we find in a limited number in nature. If we examine the shapes of crystals, we find that they are solids with faces all alike, and the transition from one face to another gives a set of changes which make a group. For we arrive at all the faces from *any* particular one by the *same* set of changes, just as we can derive by the same rational expressions every root of a normal equation from any one. There are only thirty-two types of crystals, however, so the long list of groups is not very much used by nature. Groups of operators they are frequently called. We might set them on a stage and call them dance-patterns.

This opens to us also the meaning of the realm of geometry. It was Klein, in his address at Erlangen, who pointed out that every type of geometry was a listing of what did not change in the transition from one figure to another under given conditions. Projective geometry with all its beauty is one of these systems of rhythmic change. Inversion geometry, conformal geometry, and other Cremona geometries are also examples. The bewildering arrays of forms begin to come into order and their relations are easily apparent.

But we have still more extensive riches in the motricities of rhythm, for we are now in the field of linear operators, with their fundamental functions. This gives us the power to handle wave-mechanics, and in fact wave-mechanics is in essence the study of the rhythms of the so-called ψ-functions of modern physics. But again what the mathematician studies is infinitely more than the physicist can use. The creative ability of the spirit of man finds its outlet in the creation of ideals. And in the process much knowledge which was considered valuable is swept away, for that which in modern times is worth saving in these outflowerings of the spirit is more far-reaching in its usefulness, more condensed, more generalized, more suggestive.

IV. Order

Another element in the structure of beauty we call order. Order was early in its appearance to man. When he studied a square, he found that all the angles at the corners were alike. The diagonals had the same length. They crossed each other, making angles like those in the corners. Also, if he made squares on the three sides of a right triangle, that on the hypotenuse could be made exactly out of pieces of the smaller squares on the sides. Diagram after diagram was investigated, and the collection of theorems they found was put together by Euclid. Geometry it was called, for it could be used in surveying. But this practical side was scorned by the real artists. When a student who had learned a new theorem in Plato's Akadême asked what use he could make of it, the master called a slave and said: "Give him twopence, since he must make money out of what he learns." They considered the various forms of order they discovered as sacred, and not for the common herd of human cattle. These subtle connections in figures became more and more elaborate as time passed. Perhaps we should end the Greek geometry with the investigation of Apollonius on the figure made by circles tangent to three given circles. When another young French genius, named Pascal, discovered the famous theorem bearing his name, he had an order which includes all the properties of conic sections. If we select any six points on an ellipse and number them in any way, 1, 2, 3, 4, 5, 6, then joint 1,2 and 4,5 and find where the lines intersect, then 2,3 and 5,6, and find the intersection, and finally 3,4 and 6,1 and find the intersection, the three points of intersection will always line on a straight line called a Pascal line. Since the six points can be numbered in sixty different ways, there are sixty Pascal lines. These go by fours through forty-five points called Kirkman points, three on each Pascal line. The diagram becomes more and more complicated. And we could have used a circle or a parabola or a hyperbola or even two straight lines in a plane, instead of the ellipse, with like results.

There is order of course in any vision of an artist. If we put together tones we find both horizontal and vertical orders for them. We study this in counterpoint. If we examine an abstraction of Picasso's, the colored triangles, rods, violins and other forms have an order which is the real essence of the picture. Stravinsky's compositions might seem chaotic, but they have a subtle order. Any system of theorems about the products of art may be called the list of order patterns found.

Man reached beyond the world of sense again in this region, too. For the puzzling parallel axiom ultimately led Lobachevsky to try to see where the contradiction would enter if he made a geometry in which this assumption was left out. The result was startling, for much to his surprise and delight, he created a new world. One non-Euclidean geometry had been born, and now there are many. It was found that psychologically we are built on the non-Euclidean plan, and the very simple constructions of Euclid were utterly non-existent for our senses. Many painters unconsciously make use of this now in what looks like queer perspective and outlandish arrangements. However, they are giving visible form to ideas in order that express new visions of beauty. In music, the drama, the dance, we find it also. And even in poetry non-Euclidean arrangements seem to be necessary. Gertrude Stein has experimented with many.

We go further, however, for man is not contented with the order he gets from a two-way system or a three-way system. He has created four-dimensional geometry, and even has dreamed of a universe for himself which is four-dimensional. He tries to put length, breadth, thickness and depth into one figure. At any rate, in architectural ornamentation Claude Bragdon has shown the beauty in traceries that depend on four-dimensional order. The relativity theory at first tried to coordinate space as we see it, and the flow through time as we feel it, and thus have a four-dimensional space-time world. In such a world every human life would be a complete, finished, predetermined, static thing. Our appearance in the world of others would be like the figure made on the surface of a pond, if we should gradually and smoothly draw up a solid object from the bottom of the pond. And if four dimensions, let us also have five, six, a million, an infinity.

Then, too, these order-relations do not have to be seen in space forms. We can find them in algebraic expressions as related to one another, and it was a brilliant day for the mathematical artist when Descartes said, "Geometry and algebra are one." Indeed, most geometry to-day is the study of algebraic expressions, in a geometric language. As an example of algebraic order, the product of sums of two squares is the sum of two squares, the product of sums of four squares is the sum of four squares, likewise for eight squares.

If we pass from the patterns we find for order, to the motricities, the flowing types of order, we also have inexhaustible riches. We call these "algebras." When Hamilton saw four worlds of rhythms, arranged in the quaternion algebra, the human spirit had been liberated into an entirely new universe. Equations could now have not only the flower-clusters of Galois as solutions, but each petal itself became a new world, and there were flower-clusters of universes. Every equation now has but one root, very complicated it is true, but unity has been restored to the theory. And unity is one of the essential elements of beauty. These hyper-algebras have been found in the last decade in the problems of physics, and indeed without hyper-algebras physics would not have solved its problems even in the partial manner they have been handled. In the simple case of complex numbers, Steinmetz pointed out that alternating theory could be brought into unity with direct theory in their laws, by considering that each current, electromotive force and impedance was really a single complex entity and not two independent entities. It is complex algebra that slides along a power line, or sings in the radio. And hyper-algebra vibrates in the levels of the spectral lines which come from Arcturus, Sirius or Antares.

The artist who combines music and mobile-color or music and the dance is a hyper-algebraist. Color and tone are two qualitatively distinct rhythms, as are tone and motion, neither can be turned into the other. To unify a composition which puts them together depends upon the synthetizing ability of the human spirit to make a unit out of the expression and is to work in hyper-algebraic relations. The modern synchronic arts try to do this difficult thing. If they fail occasionally, that means nothing. The problem is to succeed even once. Then, if we combine music, mobile-color, the dance and poetry, we have indeed a four-dimensional world to live in, and the possibilities of subtle art expression are unlimited. We get visions of beauty and of infinity and of eternity. Ruth St. Denis consciously, or unconsciously, has some such vision as her guiding star. In mathematical forms, however, each dimension may be turned into any other. And this is the complete triumph of this mode of art.

V. Design

Another element in the structure of beauty is design. This is the arrangement of things, the way they are combined. The series of colors in the rainbow is a design. The stars of snowflakes are designs. The frost gardens on the window-pane are designs. We find a design made up of repeated elements which are alike, as the ripples that play over the surface of a lake, the many spirals of the pine cone, the call of the whip-poor-will. Or we may find a design in the fading terms of an arithmetic series. Design may be combined with rhythm, either periodic or cadenced. Or design may occur in a continuous series. The tangent lines of a circle constitute a design, the definition being that each is at the same fixed distance from the center. The Grand Canyon is a design, so is the Painted Desert, and so is the uranium atom. Clouds execute designs that may float across the sapphire sky, or they may wind like wraiths through the canyons of the mountains. Cloud shadows make designs across the slopes. And in Georgia O'Keeffe's wonderful designs the flowing rhythms of wind, water, flame and mountains constitutes the picture. The label is of no importance. In the brilliant diagrams of Kandinsky color-design is the prominent feature. The statues of Archipenko are designs, not portraits, and in a large collection of mathematical models of surfaces, we may find statues much like those of Archipenko. When we divest our art form of the representative character, do not try to imitate objects, undertake in short to be abstract artists, then we can see design more easily. In the American Indian art we have come to appreciate this kind of design, often of high order. In sheer music we have abstract design perhaps for our day at its highest. Abstract art as it is to-day is an emphasis on design, whether it be in John G. Fletcher's poetry, in "Pelléas and Mélisande," in the marvelous dream of Eliel Saarinen for a city building, in an abstraction of Duchamp-Villon, in Russell's Synchromie Cosmique, in a composition of mobile color, in the Fire-Bird of Stravinsky, or in an abstract dance—poetry and music in motion—in all these we find or should find design. In many branches of mathematics we are studying purely the structure of design.

If we consider the points of a circle we have a design of points, so for any locus of points. If we consider the tangents of an ellipse we have a design of lines, and so for any envelope. The description of the design may be very brief, as in the differential equation $y\,dx - x\,dy = 0$ we are merely saying: Draw all the straight lines in a plane that go through a fixed point, like the spokes of a wheel. In the equation $y\,dx + x\,dy = 0$ we are saying: Draw all the equilateral hyperbolas with two given perpendicular lines for asymptotes. In the equation $x\,dx + y\,dy = 0$ we are saying: Draw all concentric circles with given center. In the differential equation $(y - px)^2 = \dfrac{c^2 p^2}{1 + p^2}$ we are saying: Draw the lines which will always have a fixed amount cut off between the coordinate axes. They are the tangents of the astroid. In polyhedra we have designs, as the polyhedra whose faces are equal equilateral triangles, which may be the regular tetrahedron, octahedron or ikosahedron. If the faces are equal squares, the figure is a cube. If they are equal regular pentagons it is the dodekahedron. In case the faces are equal rhombuses, we have the rhombic dodekahedron or the triacontahedron. In the undistorted crystal, we have polyhedra whose faces are all alike. There are thirty-two large classes with many special cases. All the Archimedes polyhedra are designs. If we make a design by repeating the elementary crystals, as does nature, we find some 230 lattice forms.

If we turn to arithmetic, we may study congruences, which are designs, in which all integers are arranged according to their remainder when divided by the module. With twelve as the module, there are twelve residue systems, and of these four, namely, those of one, five, seven and eleven, constitute a special system called the totitives of twelve. Their products will always be totitives, and the list may be generated from five and seven alone. The designs in theory of number become very elaborate. Higher number theory is on the frontier of mathematical evolution. We may take congruences of algebraic forms in the same way. If the module is $x^2 + 1$, then the residues are all numbers, all multiples of x and all forms ax + b. If we combine them we call them "complex numbers." All numbers of a residue class are equivalent.

If we turn from design patterns to design motricities, we find plenty of examples. The musician creates a fugue, which is essentially a design motricity from a theme or themes to the various forms they are to appear in. If a painter repeats a triangle in differing colors and shapes, he has a design motricity. It is not the shapes and colors that are important, but the change from one to another. Hebrew poetry is largely a motricity design, enunciating a statement which is repeated in different forms to give new suggestions:

One that ruleth over men righteously,
That ruleth in the fear of God,
He shall be as the light of the morning when the sun shineth.
A morning without clouds;
When the tender grass springeth out of the earth,
Through clear shining after rain.

In transformation groups we find motricities, and any mathematical process of combination is a motricity design.

New designs appear in the development of any art. For instance, in music there were tones, then the tonic, the dominant, the sub-dominant, the major chord, the minor chord, augmented triads, diminished triads, counterpoint, dissonances. The painter learned how to make color vibrate, and even tried to show motion, as in the famous "Nude descending a staircase." In the dance a new expression for the mystic's ecstasy was created, and the rapture of the worshipper of beauty. In mathematics were created non-Archimedean number, infinitesimals—the monads of Leibniz —algebraic fields, automorphic functions, discontinuous functions, nilpotent algebras. What must be created next is a mathematics of consciousness, a theory in which x does not represent a range of values but a range of overlapping moments.

The general theory of rhythm is abstract arithmetic and abstract groups; the general theory of order is abstract geometry and abstract hyper-algebra; the general theory of design is abstract tactic and abstract algorithms; and for the next element, the general theory of harmony is abstract logic and abstract dialectic.

VI. Harmony

We consider the fourth element of the structure of beauty —harmony. On the purely knowledge side it is called consistency. Those harmonies in ideas which we perspicate as worth preserving we call propositions. From these we arrive at concepts, relations, classes, and as one of the very large branches of mathematics—logic. So important a part is it that in 1901 Bertrand Russell went so far as to assert that mathematics is symbolic logic. And for some two decades this simple assertion was so pleasing to the esthetic sense of mathematicians it was often adopted as the final statement of what mathematics is. But the statement has been shown so often to be inadequate that new definitions have been expressed. Indeed, it is so far incorrect that we must assert that in place of mathematics being logic, symbolic logic is only one phase of mathematics. This is all the more evident when we look at the new logics created in the last decade. "To be or not to be" is no longer the list of possibilities, for it must read now, "to be or not to be or to—what?" Brouwer's work along these lines is very new, and not yet widely read. We still do not consider as harmonious being and non-being, but as a choice between them there are other alternatives. The dichotomy and law of excluded middle of Aristotle, which held the world so long in fetters, are now seen to be but one way of thinking, and the human spirit is creating new ways.

What this may mean philosophically is for the future to work out. The law of identity too is gone, and no thing or event is ever again what it has once been. The saying of Heraclitos many centuries ago is seen to be true: "I can never step into the same stream twice."

Consistency is in a curious situation, for there is no test, no criterion, of consistency. We have not noticed so far any inconsistency in ordinary Euclidean geometry, for an instance, but what the future may bring forth we do not know, and the entire structure may some day be seen to be consistent only under conditions not yet stated. There is no criterion for harmony either. What is inharmonious to one age or one people is harmonious to another. Even Schoenberg's dissonances produce a harmony not thought of before. The universe in short is evolving, that is, changing from time to time, and place to place, and man is evolving and acquiring new intuitive power. Indeed, we find the solutions offered by poets, prophets and artists for the desperate problem of evil are solutions which practically say that there is really only harmony in the world and what we call evil is a kind of harmony we have not yet come to see through. It is part of a design we do not comprehend. But harmony was recognized away back in Pythagoras' time as one of the most desired goods; indeed, he says that when we appreciate harmony we shall become as gods.

That we can learn to see deeper harmonies we might exemplify in this way. If we consider a circle, we see of course that every point on it is at the same distance from the center as every other point. This is harmony. But if we project the circle, that is, take its shadow as it is held in different positions in front of a brilliant point of light, the circle becomes an ellipse or a parabola or a hyperbola, and the center becomes a point which is no longer center for anything. The harmony remains, however. The trouble is with our first statement. For if we avoid the word distance, and substitute terms from projective geometry, the center being the pole of the line at infinity, then we see that all statements remain unchanged. If we call the center the intersection of conjugate diameters, the new statement is the same. The harmony remains, but it must be seen from a more exalted standpoint.

We must consider harmony motricities too, and on the consistency side they are the modes of inference we use, the patterns of deductions, whether ordinary inferring or such subtle inferences as those Fermat used so effectively three centuries ago. The essence of these, commonly called "mathematical induction," is simply the intuition of that part of a set of particular facts, which remains independent of other parts. To use James's example, if I say that on a Royal Baking Powder can, the wrapper has a picture of a Royal Baking Powder can, then I know at once that inside that is another picture, and another, and so on to any extent. Or again the lines that connect in succession the midpoints of the sides of a rectangle make a rhombus, and the lines that connect the midpoints of the sides of a rhombus make a rectangle; therefore, if I continue drawing such lines I will forever have a rectangle or a rhombus. The edges that join the centers of the faces of a cube make an octahedron, and the edges that connect the centers of its faces make a cube. Hence the conclusion. But we can go further, and state that in a certain figure we have drawn with yellow crayon and labeled an isosceles triangle, the equality of the sides demands as harmonious the equality of the two base angles. And since this fact is independent of the size of the triangle, or its particular shape, or its color, we may say that in any isosceles triangle the base angles will be equal. It is easy to see that most mathematical reasoning is of this intuitive and we may say, Fermatian character, which was pointed out some years ago by Poincaré.

As an example of what is meant here by harmony motricity we can cite the symphony in music. It is a composition of many parts, very elaborate sometimes, yet all in harmony. In grand opera we have another example. The theory of rational mechanics is another case, very largely ideal, and treating of situations, forces, and laws not known to exist in nature, but so harmonious a system that physicists were very reluctant to dispense with it, and even yet cling to Hamilton's principle as the one key to all modern relativity physics.

One of the most magnificent attempts at the production of harmony in mathematical subjects is shown in the late E. H. Moore's "General Analysis." For several years he worked on this unifying theory, and in the course of time all his researches will be published. It brings together in a mathematical symphony every part of analysis, so that we deal with a finite number of variables, a denumerable number, or a non-denumerable infinity, all at the same time. It uses matrix theory for explaining any type of integration; and rationality domains, hypercomplex domains, functional domains, all appear to play their rôles.

VII. Conclusion

We now return to the original question: What is mathematics? We are able to say that in the spirit of man, a living, constantly changing, elusive entity, there are elements which produce art and knowledge. If we study what they produce, we find that it is called beauty, and contains elements which we may consider either from the living, dynamic side as elements in the structure as viewed by the artist; or we may look at them from the static side, as knowledge, and name them rhythm, order, design and harmony. Mathematics is, on the artistic side, a creation of new rhythms, orders, designs and harmonies, and on the knowledge side, is a systematic study of the various rhythms, orders, designs and harmonies. We may condense this into the statement that mathematics is, on one side, the qualitative study of the structure of beauty, and on the other side is the creator of new artistic forms of beauty. The mathematician is at once creator and critic, not always, of course, in the same person. It is well known that Sylvester, Klein and Poincaré were great creators, and not much interested in the critical side. Cayley, Hilbert and Picard were magnificent examples of the critical side. Sylvester never knew in a new set of lectures where he would go. Klein was the despair of Hilbert with his flashes of intuitive creation, using any medium for expression that met his fancy. Poincaré always attacked his work with the intuitive eye. But in all great mathematicians from Pythagoras to Poincaré we find the artist character combined in varying degree with the scholar character.

We may also now answer the second question: Why should mathematics interest more than a few? Mary Austin in her "Everyman's Genius" advises all creative artists to study higher mathematics, so does Havelock Ellis. Not of course for the mere scholarship involved, not for the keen intelligence it will promote, but for the high order of imagination it will demand, for the incisive artistic insight it will generate. If, for instance, one studies only the fields in algebraic number which are superquadratic, having groups of order 2^N, he will learn new things about beauty. If he studies only the field of symmetric algebraic forms he will be charmed with its elegant beauty. The algebra of determinants is a beautiful garden, open on every side to expansion, as one may see in Metzler's treatise. If he finds some new theorems in the geometry of the triangle, he will be thrilled with their beauty. Merely to know of the transversals of a triangle, the Brocard points and Brocard circle, the Lemoine circle, the nine-point-circle, the Tucker circles, the isotomic lines, the isogonal lines and other figures, will bring new beauty to the imagination. In theory of numbers Fermat's last theorem awaits its proof, and will crown with glory the one who gives the proof. Dickson's division algebras furnish a very interesting and profitable realm for new theorems. Why extend the list? It is endless.

Many mathematicians have been artists in other ways. Some wrote poetry, some composed music. The inquiry conducted several years ago into mathematicians' activities found that most of them were seriously interested in some phase of art. And most of them reported that their discoveries or creations came just as do the inspirations of artists in other lines. The mathematician dreams, and in his dream an elusive spirit goes in and out; floats in the mist, and vanishes; glides back at unexpected moments, but slips away from the hand that would grasp her; reappears in an intricate dance, and phantasmal play of color; disappears; and one day steps out to clasp the hand that has awaited her, with Kummer's ideal numbers for a gift. The mathematician dreams and in the spinning chaos fairy flowers in fantastic forms bloom and vanish; mists wind through them with birds flashing now and then; strains like Debussy's nocturnes are faintly heard; a seething, bewildering multitude of forms are created out of the void, they drop back into the void; and then in one rapturous moment a new form appears, superbly beautiful, and Prospero's wand is held stationary to bid the cloud-castle, the flowers, the wild birds, the haunting music, the spirits of light and beauty stay, and a new branch of mathematics is born, the linear associative algebra of Benjamin Peirce. This is an enchanted land, and the city, like Hugh Ferriss' "Metropolis of Tomorrow," is, in Tennyson's words, "built to music, therefore never built at all, and therefore built forever." It is a world that knows no second law of thermodynamics, a world that guarantees to man his creative nature, his eternity of time, his imperishability. Here grows the ash-tree Yggdrasill, supporting the universe, its roots in nature, its trunk of the fibers of logic, its foliage in clearest ether of intuition, its inflorescence the living imagination. In this land of enchantment the queen is beauty, who turns men into gods.

NOTES

[1] J. G. Fletcher, "White Symphony."
[2] J. Cheney, "The New World Architecture," p. 347.

MATHEMATICS AS AN ART

J. W. N. SULLIVAN

The late J. W. N. Sullivan was one of the ablest interpreters of science and mathematics of recent times, a masterful exponent of the art of scientific popularization. As a young man he obtained a substantial training in mathematics and the physical sciences in a polytechnical school. During those formative years he had quietly attained an unsurpassed understanding of contemporary science. Remarkably well read in mathematics, and equally at home in music, he was more than well equipped for his unique mission. Possessed of an extraordinary ability to sense the crux of a complex set of ideas, he placed an unerring finger upon the fundamental significance of scientific and mathematical concepts.

As Sullivan himself has pointed out, scientific ideas have a history. They come into being in response to certain human needs—needs which, interestingly enough, are by no means limited to scientists. In order to appreciate the full import of these ideas, they must be examined in the light of man's overall intellectual, aesthetic, and spiritual activities.

The present essay is representative of the disarming simplicity and profound humanism that characterize all of Sullivan's writing. Among his best works are Aspects of Science (First Series); History of Mathematics in Europe; The Limitations of Science; Isaac Newton; *and* Beethoven.

Mathematics as an Art*

THE PRESTIGE enjoyed by mathematicians in every civilized country is not altogether easy to understand. Anything which is valued by the generality of men is either useful or pleasant, or both. Farming is a valued occupation, and so is piano-playing, but why are the activities of the mathematician considered to be important? It might be said that mathematics is valued for its applications. Everybody knows that modern civilization depends, to an unprecedented extent, upon science, and a great deal of that science would be impossible in the absence of a highly developed mathematical technique. This is doubtless a weighty consideration; and it is true that even mathematics has benefited by the increased esteem in which science is held as a consequence of the magnificent murderous capacities it exhibited in the late war. But it is doubtful whether this consideration alone is adequate to explain the exalted position accorded to mathematics throughout a larger part of its history. On the other hand, it does not seem as if we could attach much importance to the claim made by many mathematicians that their science is a delightful art. Their claim is doubtless justified; but the fact that a few, a very few, unusual individuals obtain great pleasure from some incomprehensible pursuit is no reason why the ordinary man should admire them and support them. Chess professorships are not established, but there are probably more people who appreciate the "beauties" of chess than appreciate the beauties of mathematics. The present position accorded to mathematics by the non-mathematical public is due partly to the usefulness of mathematics and partly to the persistence, in a more or less vague form, of old and erroneous ideas respecting its real significance. It is only within quite recent times, indeed, that the correct status of mathematics has been discovered, although there are many and very important aspects of this wonderful activity which still remain mysterious.

It is probable that mathematics originated with Pythagoras.

* Reprinted from J. W. N. Sullivan, *Aspects of Science: Second Series*, 1926, pp. 80–96. By permission of Alfred A. Knopf, Inc.

There is no clear evidence that that distinctive activity we call mathematical reasoning was fully recognized and practised by any one before Pythagoras. Certain arithmetical results had long been known, of course, but neither geometry nor algebra had been created. The geometrical formulas used by the ancient Egyptians, for example, deal chiefly with land-surveying problems, and were evidently obtained empirically. They are usually wrong and are nowhere accompanied by proofs. It seems strange that this particular possibility of the mind should have been discovered so late, for it is completely independent of external circumstances. Even music, the most independent of what are usually classed as the arts, is more dependent on its *milieu* than is mathematics. Nevertheless, both music and mathematics, the two most "subjective" of human creations, have been singularly late and slow in their development. And just as it is impossible for us to understand what their rudimentary music meant to the Greeks, so it is impossible to enter into the difficulties of the pre-mathematical mind. The musical enthusiasms of Plato are just as remote from us as are the difficulties of that Chinese Emperor who could not be convinced by the abstract proof that the volume of a sphere varies as the cube of its radius. He had various sized spheres made, filled with water, and weighed. This was his conception of a proof. And this must have been typical of the ancient mind. They lacked a faculty, just as the Greeks lacked a harmonic sense.

It is not surprising, therefore, that when the mind first became aware of this unsuspected power it did not understand its true nature. It appeared vastly more significant—or at least significant in a different way from what it really is. To the Pythagoreans, overwhelmed by the æsthetic charm of the theorems they discovered, number became the principle of all things. Number was supposed to be the very essence of the real; other things that could be predicted of the real were merely aspects of number. Thus the number one is what, in a certain aspect, we call reason, for reason is unchangeable, and the very essence of unchangeableness is expressed by the number one: the number two, on the other hand, is unlimited and indeterminate; "opinion" as contrasted with "reason," is an expression of the number two: again, the proper essence of marriage is expressed in the number five, since five is reached by combining three and two, that is, the first masculine with the first feminine number: the number four is the essence of justice, for four is the product of equals. To understand this outlook it is only necessary to enter into that condition of mind which takes any analogy to represent a real bond. Thus odd and even, male and female, light and darkness, straight and curved, all become expressions of some profound principle of opposition which informs the world. There are many mystical and semi-mystical writers of the present day who find themselves able to think in this manner; and it must be admitted that there is a not uncommon type of mind, otherwise orthodox, which is able to adopt this kind of reasoning without discomfort. Even Goethe, in his *Farbenlehre*, finds that a triangle has a mystic significance.

As long as the true logical status of mathematical propositions remained unknown it was possible for many mathematicians to surmise that they must have some profound relation to the structure of the universe. Mathematical propositions were supposed to be true quite independently of our minds, and from this fact the existence of God was deduced. This doctrine was, indeed, a refinement on the Pythagorean fantasies, and was held by many who did not believe in the mystic properties of numbers. But the mystical outlook on numbers continued to flourish for many centuries. Thus St. Augustine, speaking of the perfection of the number six, says:

> Six is a number perfect in itself, and not because God created all things in six days; rather the inverse is true, that God created all things in six days because this number is perfect, and it would remain perfect, even if the work of the six days did not exist.

From speculations of this sort the Pythagorean doctrine developed, on the one hand, in a thoroughly respectable philosophic manner into the doctrine of necessary truths, and on the other descended to cabbalistic imbecilities. Even very good mathematicians became cabbalists. The famous Michael Stifel, one of the most celebrated algebraists of the sixteenth century, considered that by far the most important part of his work was his cabbalistic interpretation of the prophetic books of the Bible. That this method enjoyed a high prestige is sufficiently shown by the general belief accorded to his prophecy that the world would come to an end on October 3, 1533—with the result that a large number of people abandoned their occupations and wasted their substance, to find when the date came and passed, that they were ruined. Such geometric figures as star-polygons, also, were supposed to be of profound significance; and even Kepler, after demonstrating their mathematical properties with perfect rigour, goes on to explain their use as amulets or conjurations. As another instance of the persistence of this way of regarding mathematical entities it may be mentioned that the early development of infinite series was positively hampered by the exaggerated significance attached to mathematical operations. Thus in the time of Leibnitz it was believed that the sum of an infinite number of zeros was equal to ½; and it was attempted to make this obvious idiocy plausible by saying that it was the mathematical analogue of the creation of the world out of nothing.

There is sufficient evidence, then, that there has existed a widespread tendency to attribute a mystic significance to mathematical entities. And there are many indications, even at the present day, that this tendency persists. It is probable, then, that the prestige enjoyed by the mathematician is not altogether unconnected with the prestige enjoyed by any master of the occult. The position accorded to the mathematician has been, to some extent, due to the superstitions of mankind, although doubtless it can be justified on rational grounds. For a long time, particularly in India and Arabia, men became mathematicians to become astronomers, and they became astronomers to become astrologers. The aim of their activities was superstition, not science. And even in Europe, and for some years after the beginning of the Renaissance, astrology and kindred subjects were important justifications of mathematical researches. We no longer believe in astrology or mystic hexagons and the like; but nobody who is acquainted with some of the imaginative but non-scientific people can help suspecting that Pythagoreanism is not yet dead.

When we come to consider the other justification of mathematics derived from the Pythagorean outlook—its justification on the ground that it provided the clearest and most indubitable examples of necessary truths—we find this outlook, so far from being extinct, still taught by eniment professors of logic. Yet the non-Euclidean geometries, now a century old, have made it quite untenable. The point of view is well expressed by Descartes in a famous passage from his Fifth Meditation:

"J'imagine un triangle, encore qu'il n'y ait peut-être en aucun lieu du monde hors de ma pensée une telle figure et qu'il n'y en ait jamais eu, il ne laisse pas néanmoins d'y avoir une certaine nature ou forme, ou essence déterminée de cette figure, laquelle est immuable et éternelle, que je n'ai point inventée et qui ne dépend en aucune façon de mon esprit; comme il paraît, de ce que l'on peut démontrer diverses propriétés de ce triangle, à savoir que ses trois angles sont égaux à deux, droits, que le plus grand angle est soutenu par le plus grand côté, et autres semblades, lesquelles maintenant, soit que je le veuille ou non, je reconnais très clairement et très évidemment être en lui, encore que je n'y aie pensé auparavant en aucune façon, lorsque je me suis imaginé la première fois un triangle, et, pourtant, on ne peut pas dire que je les ai feintes ni inventées."

A triangle, therefore, according to Descartes, does not depend in any way upon one's mind. It has an eternal and immutable existence quite independent of our knowledge of it. Its properties are discovered by our minds, but do not in any way depend upon them. This way of regarding geometrical entities lasted for two thousand years. To the Platonists geometrical propositions, expressing eternal truths, are concerned with the world of Ideas, a world apart, separate from the sensible world. To the followers of St. Augustine these Platonic Ideas became the ideas of God; and to the followers of St. Thomas Aquinas they became aspects of the Divine Word. Throughout the whole of scholastic philosophy the necessary truth of geometrical propositions played a very important part; and, as we have said, there are certain philosophers of the present day who regard the axioms of Euclid's geometry as unescapable truths. If this outlook be justified, then the mathematical faculty gives us access, as it were, to an eternally existing, although not sensible, world. Before the discovery of mathematics this world was unknown to us, but it nevertheless existed, and Pythagoras no more invented mathematics than Columbus invented America. Is this a true description of the nature of mathematics? Is mathematics really a body of knowledge about an existing, but supersensible, world? Some of us will be reminded of the claims certain theorists have made for music. Some musicians have been so impressed by the extraordinary impression of *inevitability* given by certain musical works that they have declared that there must be a kind of heaven in which musical phrases already exist. The great musician discovers these phrases—he hears them, as it were. Inferior musicians hear them imperfectly; they give a confused and distorted rendering of the pure and celestial reality. The faculty for grasping celestial music is rare; the faculty for grasping celestial triangles, on the other hand, seems to be possessed by all men.

These notions, so far as geometry is concerned, rest upon the supposed necessity of Euclid's axioms. The fundamental postulates of Euclidean geometry were regarded, up to the early part of the nineteenth century, by practically every mathematician and philosopher, as necessities of thought. It was not only that Euclidean geometry was considered to be the geometry of existing space—it was the necessary geometry of any space. Yet it had quite early been realized that there was a fault in this apparently impeccable edifice. The well-known definition of parallel lines was not, it was felt, sufficiently obvious, and the Greek followers of Euclid made attempts to improve it. The Arabians also, when they acquired the Greek mathematics, found the parallel axiom unsatisfactory. No one doubted that this was a necessary truth, but they thought there should be some way of deducing it from the other and simpler axioms of Euclid. With the spread of mathematics in Europe came a whole host of attempted demonstrations of the parallel axiom. Some of these were miracles of ingenuity, but it could be shown in every case that they rested on assumptions which were equivalent to accepting the parallel axiom itself. One of the most noteworthy of these investigations was that of the Jesuit priest Girolamo Saccheri, whose treatise appeared early in the eighteenth century, Saccheri was an extremely able logician, too able to make unjustified assumptions. His method was to develop the consequences of denying Euclid's parallel axiom while retaining all the others. In this way he expected to develop a geometry which should be self-contradictory, since he had no doubt that the parallel axiom was a necessary truth. But although Saccheri struggled very hard he did not succeed in contradicting himself; what he actually did was to lay the foundations of the first non-Euclidean geometry. But even so, and although D'Alembert was expressing the opinion of all the mathematicians of his time in declaring the parallel axiom to be the "scandal" of geometry, no one seems seriously to have doubted it. It appears that the first mathematician to realize that the parallel axiom could be denied and yet a perfectly self-consistent geometry constructed was Gauss. But Gauss quite realized how staggering, how shocking, a thing he had done, and was afraid to publish his researches. It was reserved for a Russian, Lobachevsky, and a Hungarian, Bolyai, to publish the first non-Euclidean geometry. It at once became obvious that Euclid's axioms were not necessities of thought, but something quite different, and that there was no reason to suppose that triangles had any celestial existence whatever.

The further development of non-Euclidean geometry and its application to physical phenomena by Einstein have shown that Euclid's geometry is not only not a necessity of thought but is not even the most convenient geometry to apply to existing space. And with this there has come, of course, a profound change in the status we ascribe to mathematical entities, and a different estimate of the significance of the mathematician's activities. We can start from any set of axioms we please, provided they are consistent with themselves and one another, and work out the logical consequences of them. By doing so we create a branch of mathematics. The primary definitions and postulates are not given by experience, nor are they necessities of thought. The mathematician is entirely free, within the limits of his imagination, to construct what worlds he pleases. What he is to imagine is a matter for his own caprice; he is not thereby discovering the fundamental principles of the universe nor becoming acquainted with the ideas of God. If he can find, in experience, sets of entities which obey the same logical scheme as his mathematical entities, then he has applied his mathematics to the external world; he has created a branch of science. Why the external world should obey the laws of logic, why, in fact, science should be possible, is not at all an easy question to answer. There are even indications in modern physical theories which make some men of science doubt whether the universe will turn out to be finally rational. But, however that may be, there is certainly no more reason to suppose that natural phenomena must obey any particular geometry than there is to suppose that the music of the spheres, should we ever hear it, must be in the diatonic scale.

Since, then, mathematics is an entirely free activity, unconditioned by the external world, it is more just to call it an art than a science. It is as independent as music of the external world; and although, unlike music, it can be used to illuminate natural phenomena, it is just as "subjective," just as much a product of the free creative imagination. And it is not at all difficult to discover that the mathematicians are impelled by the same incentives and experience the same satisfactions as other artists. The literature of mathematics is full of æsthetic terms, and the mathematician who said that he was less interested in results than in the beauty of the methods by which he found the results was not expressing an unusual sentiment.

But to say that mathematics is an art is not to say that it is a mere amusement. Art is not something which exists merely to satisfy an "æsthetic emotion." Art which is worthy of the name reveals to us some aspect of reality. This is possible because our consciousness and the external world are not two independent entities. Science has advanced sufficiently far for us to be able to say that the external world is, at least very largely, our own creation; and we understand much of what we have created by understanding the laws of our own being, the laws in accordance with which we must create. There is no reason to suppose that there is a heavenly storehouse of musical phrases, but it is true that the musician can reveal to us a reality which is profounder than that of common sense. "He who understands the meaning of my music," Beethoven is reported to have said, "shall be free from the miseries that afflict other men." We may not know what he meant, but it is evident that he regarded music as something that had meaning, something that revealed a reality which cannot normally be perceived. And it seems that the mathematician, in creating his art, is exhibiting that movement of our minds that has created the spatio-temporal material universe we know. Mathematics, as much as music or any other art, is one of the means by which we rise to a complete self-consciousness. The significance of mathematics resides precisely in the fact that it is an art; by informing us of the nature of our own minds it informs us of much that depends on our minds. It does not enable us to explore some remote region of the eternally existent; it helps to show us how far what exists depends upon the way in which we exist. We are the law-givers of the universe; it is even possible that we can experience nothing but what we have created, and that the greatest of our mathematical creations is the material universe itself.

We return thus to a sort of inverted Pythagorean outlook. Mathematics is of profound significance in the universe, not because it exhibits principles that we obey, but because it exhibits principles that we impose. It shows us the laws of our own being and the necessary conditions of experience. And is it not true that the other arts do something similar in those regions of experience which are not of the intellect alone? May it not be that the meaning Beethoven declared his music to possess is that, although man seems to live in an alien universe, yet it is true of the whole of experience as well as of that part of it which is the subject of science that what man finds is what he has created, and that the spirit of man is indeed free, eternally subject only to its own decrees? But however this may be it is certain that the real function of art is to increase our self-consciousness; to make us more aware of what we are, and therefore of what the universe in which we live really is. And since mathematics, in its own way, also performs this function, it is not only æsthetically charming but profoundly significant. It is an art, and a great art. It is on this, besides its usefulness in practical life, that its claim to esteem must be based.

Index

Index

A

Ahmes, 59
Alcuin, 18
Alkhwarizmi, 59
Ampère, A. M., 178
Apollonius, 34, 45
Aristotelian logic, 84
Aristotle, 73, 84, 256
Arithmetic, logical basis of, 102 ff.
   dual role of, 20, 21
   new interest in, 19
Arithmetica, 16–17
Arithmetiké, 16
Art, nature of, 241, 245, 272
Axiom of choice, 100
   of infinity, 105

Axioms, 76
   consistency of, 160 ff.

B

Beethoven, L. v., 272
Bell, E. T., 6
Bernays, 136, 143
Black, Max, 89
Boethius, 18
Bohr's Principle of Complementarity, 205
Bolyai, J., 74–75, 120, 271
Bombelli, 60
Boole, George, 21
Boolean algebra, 85
Boyle's Law, 189–90

N